THE TIMES
QUIZ OF
THE YEAR
1990

Compiled by
Anthony Livesey

TIMES BOOKS

Published by
TIMES BOOKS
16 Golden Square
WIR 4BN

Copyright © Times Books 1990

ISBN 0 7230 0351 3

Photoset by
Rowland Phototypesetting Limited,
Bury St Edmunds, Suffolk

Printed and bound in Great Britain by
Scotprint Limited, Musselburgh

Acknowledgements
All photographs provided by *The Times* and
Reuters with the exception of the following:
Page 13 Pic 1 John Chapman
Page 13 Pic 2 Raymond Mander and Joe
Mitchenson Theatre Collection
Page 13 Pic 4 Mercury Press Agency Limited
Page 15 Pic 3 BBC
Page 15 Pic 4 The Daily Telegraph
Page 77 Pic 3 London News Service
Page 89 Pic 2 Christopher Jones
Page 89 Pic 5 Peter West

The questions in this quiz are designed to entertain; in no way are they a test of intelligence. They are, however, a test of memory. Oliver Goldsmith, in another context, wrote, 'O Memory! thou fond deceiver' – and so it is. After even a brief passage of time, human memory, while remaining confident of outline, becomes unsure of detail.

The information needed to answer each question has appeared in *The Times* during 1990. Of necessity, the time span covered runs from January to September. Should this volume meet with public approval, future annual volumes will cover a full year – from October to September. *The Times*, however, comprises daily some 150,000 words – the length of two modern novels. How many of us can, with confident aplomb, both correctly spell the president of the Ivory Coast's surname and specify the wing span of a long-billed dowitcher?

Thus the questions may best be attempted by a group – with colleagues on a journey perhaps, or by a family after Christmas lunch, for one party may be knowledgable about sport, another world events and so on. Collectively all questions might then be correctly answered.

Those who falter may choose to console themselves by recalling the words of Virgil 'We are not all capable of everything'.

Anthony Livesey
September 1990

1 (2/1/90) On New Year's Day, controversy arose when 12 marksmen shot 170 grey squirrels in an attempt to halt their attacks on trees and shrubs. Where did the cull take place?

2 (4/1/90) On 3 January the Secretary of State for Employment resigned. Who is he and why did he resign?

3 (4/1/90) The former mistress of which MP accused him in court of causing almost £800 of damage to their flat? He was also accused of theft, of what?

4 (4/1/90) DM5000 (£1830) was donated by the West German Foreign Ministry to restore the bust and grave of which German buried in England?

5 (5/1/90) In an unprecedented gesture, the Queen appointed the son of a German World War II field marshal an honorary Commander of the British Empire for his contribution to reconciliation between the former adversaries. Who is he?

6 (6/1/90) In January it was announced that a new issue of stamps would celebrate the 150th anniversary of the penny black. In what way was this issue to be an innovation?

7 (6/1/90) By how much did house prices overall fall in the United Kingdom in the last quarter of 1989?

8 (10/1/90) More than 100 famous parents formed an organization to prevent children being lured into smoking by tobacco advertisements and other means. What is the organisation called?

9 (11/1/90) Mr Martin Ritchie, a surveyor aged 23, found—and promptly returned to their owner—four Certificates of Deposit in a London Street. What were they worth in total?

10 (12/1/90) In what way was it alleged that Foyles Bookshop in London had endangered the lives of its staff and customers?

11 (12/1/90) Of which university was it calculated that the debts of its 24 colleges would total £34 million in 1991?

12 (12/1/90) 47 Grosvenor Square, comprising 10 bedrooms, 10 bathrooms, and six reception rooms, was offered for sale. What was the asking price?

13 (13/1/90) What was stolen from a patient at St Thomas's Hospital, London, on 12 January? How was the theft made?

14 (15/1/90) British members of Alcor Life Extension, an optimistic Californian company, established a branch in the United Kingdom. What service was it offering?

15 (15/1/90) In 1990 there were 2286 high-street professional bodies of a certain type in the United Kingdom. By January 1990, mergers had reduced their number to 105. What are they?

16 (15/1/90) Security forces in Ulster shot and killed three men outside a betting shop in the Falls Road. What was the reason?

17 (16/1/90) In what unusual way did the Department of Social Security make savings in dispatching its roughly five million government letters annually by awarding a postal contract to DHL, a private carrier?

18 (16/1/90) A new craze in footwear from America reached the streets of the United Kingdom in January. What are the boots called? For what sport were they really designed and what is the novel feature of their design?

19 (16/1/90) The Country Landowners Association accused the Inland Revenue of harassment in January. What were the Revenue's 'snoop squads' trying to ascertain? What rural method of 'snooping' were the squads said to have adopted?

20 (17/1/90) Lord Ackner, a senior Lord of Appeal, claimed in the House of Lords that the courts service was a scandal and that many hearings were being cancelled. For what non-legal reason was this happening?

21 (17/1/90) More than 90 convicts in Dartmoor top security prison rioted on 13 January, several weeks before The Strangeways riot and, until then, the worst disturbance in two years, according to the prison's governor. What caused the eruption?

22 (18/1/90) A much-criticized fine of how much was imposed by a magistrate on 17 January on a man found smoking on the London Underground? What is the maximum fine that may be imposed?

23 (18/1/90) What was believed to be the first case in which allegations of poor workmanship resulted in the Crown Prosecution Service bringing a charge of manslaughter?

24 (19/1/90) Which former Conservative Party chairman found himself paying substantial damages to Miss Sara Keays this month? And why?

25 (20/1/90) Which Conservative MP was deselected by his local constituency in January and why?

1 The Royal Botanic Gardens, Kew.

2 Norman Fowler, to spend more time with his young children.

3 Ron Brown, the member for Edinburgh, Leith. He was fined £1000 for causing damage but acquitted of the theft of her underwear, jewellery and a picture frame.

4 Karl Marx, who is buried in Highgate cemetery in London.

5 Manfred Rommel, businessman and Mayor of Stuttgart, son of Field Marshal Erwin Rommel.

6 A portrait of Queen Victoria, used on the original Penny Black, appears together with the usual portrait of the Queen.

7 Two per cent, according to the Nationwide Anglia Building Society.

8 Parents Against Tobacco; the Duke of Gloucester is its president.

9 £4 million pounds.

10 By leaving 90 boxes containing books on emergency staircases, gangways and in front of fire exits. The bookshop was fined £21,750.

11 London University.

12 £15 million.

13 A three-day-old girl. The baby was taken by a woman posing as a health visitor.

14 A funerary club, that freezes the dead in the hope that future scientists can restore them to life.

15 Building societies.

16 Three hooded bandits, petty criminals carrying what were later discovered to be imitation weapons, were mistakenly thought to be IRA terrorists bent on raising funds through theft.

17 DHL takes items to Heathrow centre and sends them in bulk to such diverse places as Copenhagen, Dubai, Auckland, Sydney, Kuala Lumpur and Hong Kong, where they can be posted individually more cheaply.

18 'The Pump', costing £129:99 a pair. They were designed as basketball boots. The lining may be inflated to make a customized fit by a pump on the shoe's tongue to introduce supporting air, which can later be released through a valve in the heel.

19 The number of casual workers being employed. Tax investigators were said to hide in hedges to keep watch on a property.

20 Cash limits meant that there was no money to pay judges' hotel bills.

21 A goal was disallowed during an inmates football match.

22 25p, a sum claimed by the Director of London Transport and the police as derisory and self defeating. The maximum fine is £200.00.

23 An electrician was tried, and found guilty, for wrongly wiring a central heating system, which caused the owner's death with an electric shock.

24 Norman Tebbit. He had claimed in his book *Upwardly Mobile* that she had broken an undertaking not to comment on her relationship with his former cabinet colleague, Cecil Parkinson.

25 Sir Anthony Meyer, because he stood against Mrs Thatcher for the party leadership in December 1989.

26 (22/1/90) In January, the Cabinet decided to draw up proposed legislation for the prosecution of a group of alleged criminals. Lawyers estimated that this would instigate the biggest and most expensive criminal investigation in history. Of what are these alleged criminals accused?

27 (22/1/90) The Lord Chief Justice, Lord Lane was denounced as what kind of reptile, and by whom?

28 (23/1/90) What change did the Metropolitan Police make in its recruitment policy and why?

29 (24/1/90) In what way did the governors of Altrincham School for Girls, in Manchester, modify their rules in respect of two muslim pupils?

30 (26/1/90) During the gales of 25 January what speed did the wind reach in the UK? How many trees were estimated to have been destroyed?

31 (30/1/90) The United States announced its largest military retrenchment since 1945. How did this affect the United Kingdom?

32 (3/2/90) Which member of the Royal Family married on 2 February?

33 (7/2/90) What was the most important alteration in prison policy among those announced by the Home Secretary on 7 February?

34 (8/2/90) According to the Central Statistical Office's latest Family Expenditure Survey, what proportion of British households own a video-recorder?

35 (10/2/90) What innovative event was introduced in the 1990 Crufts Dog Show at Earl's Court which included golden retrievers, German shepherd dogs and border collies?

36 (12/2/90) Which breed of dog won the Supreme championship at Crufts Dog Show?

37 (13/2/90) On what occasion were the hearts of the British public sufficiently touched to spend £70 million, and on what was the money spent?

38 (14/2/90) What commodity did Harrods, the Knightsbridge store, announce it would stop selling from the end of April?

39 (21/2/90) On 20 February, what long-running dispute between Church and Parliament was ended with the passage of the Clergy (Ordination) Measure?

40 (22/2/90) Which politician was given lunch at the Savoy Hotel, London, attended by nearly 500 persons, to mark his 40 years as an MP?

41 (23/2/90) An unusual speeding fine was imposed by Richmond magistrates on a Miss Constance Scrafield? What was her mode of transport? How much was she fined?

42 (24/2/90) For what offence was Shell UK fined £1 million at Liverpool Crown Court?

43 (27/2/90) The 2000 occupants of which North Wales town were evacuated when it was flooded by mountainous seas caused by gale-force winds?

44 (28/2/90) Which car was voted 'Car of the Year' in awards organised by the magazine *What Car*?

45 (2/3/90) How much was it calculated that collecting the poll tax would cost?

46 (5/3/90) A report compiled by Gallup for the *New Woman* magazine, revealed that almost all patients wanted to know the truth about their condition. However, what percentage of doctors would lie to them if they thought that patients could not cope with the thought of a terminal illness?

47 (7/3/90) Who donated £10 million to Oxford University's fund-raising campaign and for what purpose?

48 (7/3/90) In what way was it thought that at least half the police forces in England and Wales would follow experimental schemes already in operation for dealing with people found in possession of illegal drugs?

49 (7/3/90) According to the RSPCA, a new cross-breed of dog is being bred in the United Kingdom. What is the new dog called? What dogs were crossed to produce it?

50 (8/3/90) Who was appointed, with effect from next year, Chief of the Defence Staff. What was unusual about his appointment?

26 Suspected Nazi war criminals, presently living in the United Kingdom.

27 A dinosaur, by Judge Pickles, a circuit judge.

28 Height requirements were dispensed with (hitherto men had to be at least 5ft 8in tall, woman 5ft 4in) to attract smaller recruits from ethnic minority groups.

29 The pupils were permitted to wear traditional headscarves in class, despite these being dangerous to themselves and others in laboratories and during PE lessons.

30 110 mph. More than three million.

31 Some 4000 American servicemen and their weaponry were to be withdrawn from three RAF bases.

32 Miss Marina Ogilvy, daughter of Sir Angus Ogilvy and Princess Alexandra, 24th in line of succession to the throne, married Mr Paul Mowatt.

33 A change in sentencing policy to ensure that hardened criminals spent longer in jail, while keeping petty offenders out of prison.

34 One in two.

35 The flyball race, taking place in the main ring. The dogs raced down the ring, then leapt over two-foot high plank jumps onto a seesaw. On one end of the seesaw there was a tennis ball in a box. The dogs were expected to flip the seesaw, catch the air-borne ball and race back over the jumps to the finish.

36 A West Highland white terrier, Champion Olac Moon Pilot ('Paddy').

37 St Valentine's Day. The money was spent on cards, postage and gifts.

38 Furs; the decision was apparently taken for purely financial reasons.

39 People who have remarried after divorce, or are married to divorced persons, will in future be able to offer themselves for ordination as priests or deacons.

40 Edward Heath, one-time Conservative Prime Minister. The event was hosted by another former Conservative leader, Lord Home of the Hirsel.

41 She was riding her horse, Patrick. Miss Scrafield was fined £50 for galloping her horse. A police constable on a motorcycle had timed her as she rode in Richmond Park and claimed that they were moving 'at a pace greater than a hand canter', the maximum speed permitted.

Subsequently (1/6/90) Miss Scrafield won her appeal against conviction after a courtroom debate as to the pace of a canter.

42 For polluting the Mersey estuary in August 1989 with 156 tonnes of crude oil, which escaped from a six-inch fracture in a corroded pipeline and fouled 12 miles of beach and foreshore.

43 Towyn. Massive waves had broken some 600 feet of sea wall.

44 The Rover 214 hatchback.

45 £300 million; the tax needs at least twice the administration required by the rating system.

46 Eighty per cent.

47 Sir Run Run Shaw, the Hong Kong millionaire-philanthropist and film producer. The money will fund an institute of Chinese studies.

48 First-time offenders would be cautioned rather than charged, and encouraged to seek counselling for less serious offences. The idea, police chiefs stated, was not 'backdoor' legalization of drugs, but because prosecution was both expensive and often counter productive.

49 Banddogs, a vicious and potentially lethal cross between American pit bull terriers and mastiffs or rottweilers.

50 General Sir Richard Vincent, who led a high-level military delegation to the USSR in 1989. Sir Richard is the first officer to be selected for the top military post without having first been a chief of the Army, Royal Navy or Royal Air Force.

51 (8/3/90) Which Tory MP was suspended from the House without pay for four weeks and why?

52 (8/3/90) A government-supported campaign by the charity Alcohol Concern found that how many million working days were lost annually through 'inappropriate' (excessive) drinking and at what cost to industry? Also, people in which job were found to be most likely to die from cirrhosis of the liver?

53 (9/3/90) In March 1990, the National Union of Mineworkers still owed how much to other unions which had sustained them during the miners' year-long-strike in 1984–85?

54 (9/3/90) Measures were announced to cut fishing of what fish by 30 per cent in the North Sea, reinforcing sharp cuts in quotas agreed by European Community fisheries ministers in December 1989 to conserve depleted stocks?

55 (9/3/90) Who wrote this? 'History will rate Margaret Thatcher as one of the 25 greatest influences on the nation's progress since William the Conqueror'?

56 (13/3/90) For the first time in 800 years, a branch of Oxford University will be sited outside the Oxford city limits, for the benefit of its ever increasing number of Japanese students. Where will the branch be?

57 (14/3/90) Who was appointed editor of *The Times* in succession to Charles Wilson, and of which newspaper had he been previously the editor?

58 (14/3/90) What standard pieces of a policeman's equipment did Scotland Yard consider scrapping? And why?

59 (15/3/90) Which Labour MP invited Militant supporters behind the anti-poll tax protests around the country into the Houses of Parliament to hold a press conference?

60 (15/3/90) Which MP, who in March was refusing to pay his poll tax, resigned the Labour whip?

61 (15/3/90) Which British minister offered to fly to Baghdad, and why, but was informed by Iraq that it 'would not be the right time for a visit'?

62 (16/3/90) Why was the bank account of Mrs Eleanor McLaughlin frozen?

63 (16/3/90) Which members of the Royal Family paid the first official visit to Nigeria since the country was granted independence nearly 30 years ago?

64 (22/3/90) The RSPCA reported its highest ever figure for cruelty to animals. In 1989 officials received how many calls and investigated how many complaints?

65 (23/3/90) Why did more than 1200 police officers from four English forces issue writs against their chief constables in relation to the 1984–5 miners' dispute?

66 (23/3/90) On what day, and for what reason, did twice as many people than on any other two days try to kill themselves?

67 (23/3/90) What reasons did Dr Robert Runcie, who did not have to retire as Archbishop of Canterbury until his 70th birthday in October 1991, give for leaving office nine months earlier? And what would he now have more time for?

68 (24/3/90) How much did the Duchess of York's second baby, a girl, weigh at birth?

69 (24/3/90) Who was appointed the new Chief Constable of the West Midlands, one of the toughest posts in British policing, in succession to Geoffrey Dear?

70 (24/3/90) The Labour Party won the Mid-Staffordshire by-election. What is the name of the successful candidate? Labour's majority of 9449 represented what percentage swing from the Conservatives at the General Election? How many Labour by-election victories over the Conservatives in the last 45 years did this make?

71 (24/3/90) What was perhaps surprising in Methodist Church membership between the number of members and recruitment to the ministry?

72 (26/3/90) Why will more than 100,000 undergraduates be exempt from paying interest on part of their student loans from September?

73 (27/3/90) Who became the first member of the Royal Family to bring a libel action to court, against whom and for what reason?

74 (28/3/90) What was astonishing about the lesson read at a valedictory service in St Paul's Cathedral for the Inner London Education Authority by Mr Neil Fletcher, the authority's Labour leader?

75 (28/3/90) Which actress was selected to fight the marginal constituency of Hampstead and Highgate for Labour at the next general election?

51 John Browne, member for Winchester, who had failed to disclose all his business interests.

52 Up to 14 million days, it was suggested, were lost each year, at an estimated cost to industry of £800 million. The 32 professional groups with above average death from cirrhosis of the liver ranged from publicans (top) to nurses (bottom), but included judges, lawyers, clergymen, doctors, dentists, authors and journalists, officers in the armed forces and bus conductors.

53 £500,000.

54 Haddock; members of the Scottish Fishermens' Federation will be worst hit by the reduction.

55 Tony Marlow, Tory MP for Northampton North, in an article on the Community Charge (Poll Tax).

56 At the port city of Kobe in Japan. Some 40 students graduating from Japanese universities will be accepted annually for a one-year arts course.

57 Simon Jenkins, who had been editor of *The Evening Standard*.

58 His whistle and chain. They had been used for more than a century, but today many younger officers have never had occasion to use a whistle because of personal radios and radio-controlled cars.

59 Dave Nellist, a Militant supporter and Labour member for Coventry South East.

60 Dick Douglas, Labour member for Dunfermline West.

61 Douglas Hurd, the Foreign Secretary, wanted to ask for clemency for Farzad Bazoft, an *Observer* journalist under sentence of death for allegedly spying. Bazoft was later hanged.

62 She had refused to pay her Community Charge bill. Mrs McLaughlin is the Lord Provost of Edinburgh and Lord Lieutenant of the city.

63 The Prince and Princess of Wales.

64 Well over one million calls were taken and nearly 83,000 complaints of cruelty investigated. There was a 30 per cent increase in cruelty to cats and a 164 per cent increase in that to farm animals. Dogs are most at risk. In 1989 the RSPCA brought 2026 successful prosecutions for cruelty, of which 1131 concerned dogs.

65 They alleged that they were collectively owed hundreds of thousands of pounds in overtime payments for policing the 1984–5 miners' dispute. The writs issued against the Chief Constable of Cleveland contained claims by 689 officers, believed to be a legal record for a lawsuit in Great Britain.

66 St Valentine's Day. The findings were reported in the *British Medical Journal* and the reason, it was thought, might be attributed to 'stress due to unrequited love'. Nearly half the cases involved adolescents and the total probably underestimated the true incidence.

67 So that there would be sufficient time for his successor 'to be known before the end of this year'. He also hoped his successor would thus be able to attend the next World Council of Churches in February and the Anglican primates' meeting in April. He would also have more time for his family and his pigs.

68 7lb 1½oz.

69 Ronald Hadfield, who since 1987 had been Chief Constable of Nottinghamshire.

70 Mrs Sylvia Heal; 21.33%. It was only Labour's 14th gain from the Conservatives in by-elections since 1945.

71 While membership fell over the past three years (by 19,000 between 1986 and 1989, bringing the total down to 432,000), recruitment to the ministry remained buoyant, around its target of 100 new ministers annually.

72 Because of an oversight by parliamentary draughtsmen who, in their haste to get the Students Loans Bill on the statute book, overlooked the fact that it is unlawful to charge interest to minors. Most of the students affected live in Scotland, where they go to a university, polytechnic or college at the age of 17 rather than 18, as in England.

73 Viscount Linley sued News (UK) Ltd, publishers of *Today* newspaper, for portraying him as 'an upper-class lager lout' who had thrown beer over some of his friends in a public house. He was awarded £35,000 damages, but waived his right so that no stigma should attach to t'ie integrity of the *Today*'s journalist.

74 Instead of reading St Luke's account of the child Jesus debating with the elders in the temple, as expected, the congregation of 2000 school children and civic dignitaries were subjected to the prophet Isaiah's brimstone denunciation of 'those who make unjust laws.'

75 Glenda Jackson.

76 (28/3/90) In what way will local authorities be allowed, as announced by Mr Christopher Chope, Under Secretary of State at the Department of the Environment, to spend £38.7 million over the next financial year to ease the housing plight of the needy and homeless?

77 (29/3/90) British and American Customs officers foiled an alleged attempt to smuggle what devices to Iraq when they arrested five people at Heathrow and in Surrey?

78 (30/3/90) On what issue did the Yeomen Warders of the Tower of London ask their union, the National Union of Civic and Public Servants, to intercede on their behalf?

79 (30/3/90) In what way did Mrs Florence Phillips, a widow aged 87, earn a place in legal history?

80 (31/3/90) What names did the Duke and Duchess of York give their second child, a girl, and how is she to be styled?

81 (31/3/90) The Chambers, at Old Square, Lincoln's Inn, is one of several to have published brochures under the Bar's new freedom to advertise. In what way did these barristers make a further break with tradition in their brochure?

82 (2/4/90) In which prison did the worst disturbances this century, it is thought, occur?

83 (2/4/90) The worst rioting in central London in 20 years occurred when a peaceful march in protest at the Community Charge was highjacked by allegedly some 3000–3500 left-wing militants, members of the Socialist Workers' Party and anarchist groups. Looting and assault ensued. How many arrests were made?

84 (2/4/90) To whom did the Crown Estate Commissioners grant a lease on Drake's Island, a rocky outcrop in Plymouth Sound, and for what purpose?

85 (3/4/90) Considerable areas of Great Britain were shaken by the second biggest earthquake to hit the country within the last 100 years. Where was the 20-second tremor centred and what, according to the seismic research group of the British Geological Survey, did it measure on the Richter scale?

86 (3/4/90) The City of London, to reduce congestion caused by street parking of cars rather than in public garages, raised its parking meter charges per hour from £1.20 to what sum?

87 (3/4/90) Why was a mother awarded £33,000 damages in the High Court for giving birth to a baby?

88 (3/4/90) It was estimated that damage to hundreds of vehicles and properties in the West End during Community Charge riots on Saturday 31 March would cost Scotland Yard and insurance companies at least how much?

89 (3/4/90) Three bottles of 1891 Livadia White port were sold at Sotheby's to an unnamed bidder for £7700. From whose cellars had the wine come?

90 (4/4/90) Drivers, conductors and engineers on London 'buses, Britain's biggest 'bus company, have always been subjected to a certain ban during and immediately prior to working hours. This ban was extended to more than 3000 white-collar staff. What is it?

91 (4/4/90) According to a survey carried out by Gallup for the Realeat Company, what percentage of Britons are now vegetarians or go out of their way to avoid eating red meat?

92 (4/4/90) Name any six of the 20 authorities which the Secretary of State designated for Community Charge capping?

93 (5/4/90) Mr Cecil Parkinson, Secretary of State for Transport, announced what innovation in the construction of the country's new road projects?

94 (5/4/90) What new scholarship financed two British fifth-formers to attend Syracuse University in New York State?

95 (6/4/90) A judicial inquiry was announced into the Strangeways Prison riots, to be led by whom?

96 (6/4/90) What decision was signalled by the School Examination and Assessment Council concerning examinations in English literature for 16-year-olds?

97 (6/4/90) What new and less stringent regulations concerning marriage between Roman Catholics and non-Catholics were announced by the Roman Catholic Church in England and Wales?

98 (7/4/90) What was unusual about the plans for a new five-star hotel in Birmingham?

99 (9/4/90) In what way did the Church of England's Liturgical Commission seek to alter the words of the National Anthem?

100 (10/4/90) In what novel way did prison authorities at Strangeways Prison, Manchester, seek to subdue rioting inmates and induce their surrender?

76 They will be able to spend that sum to encourage council tenants to leave their homes and buy on the private property market, thereby releasing, it is hoped, 2000 homes for families in need.

77 Trigger devices for nuclear bombs, due to be loaded onto an Iraqi airliner. The 40 triggers seized were dummies, specially made in Massachusetts for an 18-month undercover operation, code-named *Argos*, which began in southern California.

78 The 42 yeomen, who on average welcome 2.2 million visitors a year, asked their union to fight a proposal to open the royal palace on Sunday mornings.

79 Magistrates ruled that the nocturnal noises (snoring) emanating from her bedroom contravened the Control of Pollution Act.

80 Eugenie Victoria Helena; she will be known as Princess Eugenie of York.

81 They published the daily charging rate of its members. The guideline charging rates for a six-hour paperwork day range from £750 to £1000 for Mr Nicholas Stewart QC, with 16 years in practice, to between £150 and £250 for the newest qualified member of chambers.

82 Strangeways Prison, Manchester. The pre-planned riot over conditions began in the chapel at the end of the Sunday service.

83 Three hundred and thirty-nine. According to Scotland Yard, 298 of those arrested were male, 41 female; 227 were aged between 17 and 25 and only 196 had London addresses. The Yard further stated that 224 were employed, 115 unemployed.

84 The Trireme Trust, for it to develop the site for the construction and operation of two full-sized triremes, replicas of Greek vessels.

85 The earthquake centred on Wrexham, Clwyd, North Wales, and measured 5.2 on the Richter scale. No injuries were reported.

86 £2.

87 Mrs Kay Stranger, already mother of three children, became pregnant again and entered hospital in March 1983 for an abortion and sterilization. The sterilization was successful but doctors failed to terminate the pregnancy.

88 £10 million, probably more.

89 That of the murdered Tsar, Nicholas II.

90 Staff are now forbidden a lunchtime pint of beer or glass of wine.

91 Some 10 per cent; the main arguments given were for improved health and for moral reasons. Nearly 2,100,000 people, 3.7 per cent of the population, are total vegetarians.

92 Avon, Barnsley, Basildon, Brent, Bristol, Calderdale, Camden, Derbyshire, Doncaster, Greenwich, Hammersmith and Fulham, Haringey, Hillingdon, Islington, North Tyneside, Rochdale, Rotheram, St Helens, Southwark, and Wigan.

93 Private companies will build three new roads in the next 10 years, to be financed by toll charges. This will enable a new bridge to be built across the Severn, a relief road around the north of Birmingham and a new road linking Birmingham with Manchester.

94 They were from Lockerbie Academy on a scholarship in memory of the 270 victims of the Pam Am air disaster. Syracuse University lost 35 students returning home to the United States for Christmas when a terrorist bomb exploded on the airliner over Lockerbie.

95 Lord Justice Woolf (Sir Harry Woolf), a self-admitted liberal who describes himself as 'moderate and open-minded'.

96 The demise of the English literature set book, which for decades had introduced the young to the works of the great British authors.

97 The Catholic Church's insistence that the children of a marriage with a non-Catholic should be brought up as Catholics was maintained, but the promise of the Catholic partner no longer has to be in writing and is replaced by a verbal statement.

98 It is to be built in the shape of the former Cunard liner *Mauretania*, one time holder of the Blue Riband, built in 1906 and scrapped in 1935.

99 A more peaceable form was suggested for the anthem used at Remembrance Day services. The middle verse, little used, calling on God to 'scatter our enemies', would be replaced by an alternative verse written in 1836 by William Edward Hickson, a bootmaker, the lines of which run as follows:

> 'Nor on the land alone –
> But be God's mercies known
> From shore to shore.
> Lord, make the nation see
> That men should brothers be,
> And form one family
> The wide world o'er.'

100 Wagner's *The Ride of the Valkyrie* was amplified at full volume and aimed at the rioters.

1 (8/3/90) What point is this man making, who is he and where is he speaking?

3 (2/4/90) With whom is this little girl dancing and to what purpose?

2 (21/3/90) Who are the couple in this 1920s photograph and why was it reproduced in *The Times*?

4 (3/4/90) Why should this man be seated at a desk in a wilderness and who is he?

5 (9/6/90) Who is seemingly drowning with a soldier and how did he get where he is?

1 Mr Tony Ritchie, Mayor of Southwark, endeavouring to restore order to a council Community Charge meeting, which was later abandoned when Militant supporters invaded the chamber.

2 Tom and Kate Major, music hall artists, the parents of John Major, the newly appointed Chancellor of the Exchequer. The chancellor was due to present his first budget when the picture appeared.

3 Zoe Hodges, aged eight, is practising a tap-dancing routine with Mr Bernard Weatherill, Speaker of the Commons. They joined an attempt to break a world record and raise money for the ITV Telethon '90 in May.

4 Mr Chris Patten, the Secretary of State for the Environment. He had just announced an important employment fillip for north-west England by disclosing that a new VAT centre for all of Great Britain is to be built in Liverpool's docklands, creating up to 1000 jobs in the area.

5 Mr Tom King, the Defence Secretary, was being driven in a water-proofed Land-Rover at the Royal Marine base at Harmworthy, Dorset, where the Special Boat Service is trained. He was dressed in a wet suit while being driven through a tank 5ft deep and suffered no ill effects.

2 (27/1/90) The Prime Minister seen in convivial mood, but where is she?

1 (25/1/90) At what is Mrs Thatcher looking and where is she?

3 (23/2/90) What brought together Mrs Thatcher, Mr Weatherill, the Speaker, and Mr Kinnock and where are they?

4 (1/6/90) Where is the Prime Minister trying her hand at a drum solo?

1 The Prime Minister, pondering a modern sculpture, had just opened the Tate Gallery's new rearrangement of its exhibits.

2 Mrs Thatcher is toasting Julie Goodyear, the actress, and cast members of *Coronation Street* on the set of the Rover's Return public house at Granda Television, Manchester.

3 With MPs, peers and Westminster staff, they are singing at a recording of *Songs of Praise*, to be shown on BBC 1, at St Margaret's church, the parish church of Parliament.

4 She was visiting EMI's Abbey Road recording studios which were used by the Beatles, of whom she said she was a fan.

101 (10/4/90) Why did the visit to Great Britain of Señor Domingo Cavallo help to heal the rift between this country and Argentina following the Falklands War?

102 (10/4/90) Up to 20 public schools were considering what sort of random testing for all pupils?

103 (12/4/90) What did customs officers find and impound on the *MV Gur Mariner* on Teesside, a vessel bound for Iraq?

104 (13/4/90) What creature was given the name 'Docky' and why?

105 (14/4/90) According to Home Office research, what percentage of all female murder victims were killed by their husbands or lovers?

106 (16/4/90) According to a study reported in the *Journal of the Royal Society of Medicine*, four in five injuries from assault in the United Kingdom are caused by what means?

107 (16/4/90) An opinion poll commission by the Conservative Party and conducted by Gallup found what percentage of people in favour of the Community Charge replacing local rates?

108 (18/4/90) According to the Charity Commissions annual report, a record 4119 new charities were registered in England and Wales in 1989, bringing the total to what number?

109 (19/4/90) What famous British public school for girls announced its closure?

110 (20/4/90) Why did Mr Jeff Rooker, Labour MP for Birmingham Perry Barr, call on the Home Secretary to consider prosecuting Mr Norman Tebbit MP?

111 (25/4/90) What reverse was suffered by the anti-abortion lobby in a House of Commons vote?

112 (25/4/90) What right did local councils win at law in respect of the Community Charge?

113 (25/4/90) Which member of the 'Great Train Robbers' gang was murdered in southern Spain when shot twice in the neck?

114 (25/4/90) What community service scheme was launched by the Prince of Wales and what is its name?

115 (25/4/90) What was to be the final stage, beginning in April, of the restoration of the Palace of Westminster, which started in 1981?

116 (26/4/90) The siege of Strangeways Prison, Manchester, ended on 25 April after 25 days of rioting by prisoners. What was the estimated cost of the prolonged disturbance, in financial terms?

117 (26/4/90) What sartorial innovation marked the 550th birthday of Eton College, founded in 1440 by King Henry VI?

118 (28/4/90) Two Irishmen and a woman, convicted of being part of an IRA reconnaissance unit plotting the murder of Mr Tom King, the Secretary of State for Defence, had their convictions quashed by the Court of Appeal on what technicality?

119 (30/4/90) Oxfam complied with what ruling by the Charity Commission concerning a campaign it had launched?

120 (1/5/90) By how many votes did the Government survive a House of Commons backbench rebellion when it defeated a move to establish a compulsory nationwide registration scheme intended to control and identify dogs?

121 (1/5/90) Who did the Queen appoint to succeed Sir William Heseltine as her new private secretary?

122 (3/5/90) Which minister was moved to the Department of the Environment and promoted Minister for Local Government with responsibility for the Community Charge?

123 (5/5/90) In the local elections, the Labour Party made some 300 gains nationwide but was repulsed by the Tories in London. How many seats did the Liberal Democrats win and lose?

124 (7/5/90) In what way was London newly divided with effect from 6 May?

125 (7/5/90) A new logo to embellish police vehicles and buildings was announced by Scotland Yard to improve the London police identity. In what colours is it designed?

101 Cavallo, the Argentine Foreign Minister, was the first senior Argentine official to visit London since the conflict.

102 For drug abuse; one school at least has written to parents asking for their views.

103 Under the codename *Bertha*, this was the third Customs action in a fortnight to prevent consignments of weaponry being exported to Iraq.

104 A porpoise; she had got inside the twin lock gates of King George's Dock, Hull, and resisted all blandishments to return to the sea.

105 Nearly half, only 14 per cent being killed by strangers.

106 The use of beer glasses and bottles, broken or whole. The figure was correlated from accident and emergency centres in five large city hospitals.

107 Seventy-one per cent supported it as the fairest principle for a local government tax, provided there were reductions for the less well-off.

108 168,170, most of which are concerned with protecting the environment, and helping the disabled and victims of crime and drug abuse.

109 Cranborne Chase, second only to Roedean in prestige. High interest rates and the cost of maintaining the 18th-century building, near Tisbury in Wiltshire, were given as the reasons for the decision.

110 For supposedly inciting racial hatred, after Mr Tebbit's comment that a proportion of the Asian immigrant community failed to pass his integration test and support England, rather than their country of origin, at cricket matches.

111 The lobby's motion to achieve a reduction in the abortion limit to below 24 weeks was defeated, MPs voting on the non-whipped issue 301 to 255 to reject a 22-week limit.

112 Those councils which were Community Charge-capped were given leave to challenge the Government in the High Court.

113 Charles Wilson; the killing, for reasons yet unestablished, occurred on his 35th wedding anniversary.

114 His national scheme, called the Volunteers, supported by both the Government and trades unions, plans to recruit 1000 young people aged 16 to 24 this year to work on community projects across the country for 12 to 18 weeks.

115 Restoration of the stonework of the Victoria Tower; the work will take about four years to complete and is expected to cost some £7 million.

116 The siege, the longest and most expensive in British penal history, will have cost more than £1 million in policing alone; renovating and restoring the prison would, it was thought, cost some £50 million, while building a new establishment on the same site would cost up to £100 million.

117 Its pupils will henceforth be permitted to appear in public, at Windsor and elsewhere nearby, while wearing jeans.

118 The three, sentenced to 25 years imprisonment each in 1988, were freed after the court decided that comments on the right to silence issue made by Mr King during the trial should have led to a retrial.

119 The charity abandoned plans to campaign in favour of sanctions against South Africa, following allegations that it might have broken the law as a charity by engaging in 'undue political activity' by issuing leaflets calling for sanctions on the eve of the launch of the charity's 'Front Line Africa' campaign.

120 Twelve, MPs voting by 275 to 263 to reject the proposal. Fifty Conservative MPs defied the three-line whip. Only a promise given by an environment minister to introduce a new set of measures to improve the control of dogs saved the Government from defeat.

121 Sir Robert Fellowes, brother-in-law of the Princess of Wales.

122 Mr Michael Portillo, whose rise in the Conservative Party had been meteoric during a mere six years as an MP.

123 They lost 192 seats but gained 144, making them potentially a national force again. The Social Democrat Party, on the other hand, lost 30 seats and gained five only. Independents were equally trounced, losing 57 and gaining only 26.

124 By the advent of new telephone dialling codes. Central London – the area between Fulham to Canary Wharf and from Brixton to Kentish Town – was given the prefix 071, the remainder 081.

125 In white and a shade called 'reflex blue', a mid-blue shade between that of Prussian and Cambridge blues.

126 (7/5/90) For the second time this year, Oxford University broke with 800 years of tradition by allowing what?

127 (10/5/90) According to a Gallup survey of 50,000 people, which were the most popular choice of first name for boys and girls?

128 (10/5/90) Which ship set sail from Avonmouth on her last journey to the remote Crown colony whose name she bears?

129 (14/5/90) The removal of what object allowed an uninterrupted view of St Paul's Cathedral from Fleet Street for the first time since 1865?

130 (19/5/90) According to a report published by The Samaritans, the suicide rate among men aged between 15 and 44 has increased over the last 10 years in England and Wales from 10 to 15 per 100,000, while female rates have gradually declined to about half that number. What are the two professions seemingly most at risk?

131 (23/5/90) For what achievement did the 3rd Battalion The Queen's Regiment propose to reward its soldiers with a month's leave and £100?

132 (25/5/90) Which member of the Royal Family made the first official visit to Moscow since before the Bolshevik Revolution in 1917?

133 (29/5/90) Where were 8000 Anglicans jeered as they walked in a pilgrim procession?

134 (30/5/90) To which school, and for what reason, did the Queen grant a day's holiday in October in perpetuity?

135 (1/6/90) Which council became the first in England to take court action against people failing to pay the Community Charge?

136 (5/6/90) On what issue did the House of Lords make its biggest revolt in Mrs Thatcher's 11-year tenure as prime minister?

137 (14/6/90) Which National Trust house, just vacated by Lord McAlpine, until recently treasurer of the Conservative Party, was badly damaged by an explosion caused by the IRA?

138 (16/6/90) Which six people were created life peers in the birthday honours list?

139 (18/6/90) What measure did the government announce to help clear the homeless from the streets of London and other cities?

140 (18/6/90) A survey guide, published by Chambers & Partners, a legal recruitment agency, revealed that successful barristers, at the top of their profession, can earn £300,000 to £600,000 annually in one form of their work, but only gross £100,000 in another. Specialising in what type of legal matter earns the higher fee, and what the lesser?

141 (18/6/90) Over the week-end Cambridge inaugurated a building for which faculty?

142 (19/6/90) What did Tom King, the Defence Secretary, describe as 'the biggest cut in real terms' the armed forces had faced for a long time?

143 (19/6/90) In his will, the late multi-millionaire Sir Joseph Nickerson, left what to the Prince and Princess of Wales on the occasion of their 10th, 20th, 30th and 40th wedding anniversaries?

144 (19/6/90) Who became the first non-royal woman member of the Order of the Garder at the installation ceremony this year?

145 (20/6/90) The 90th birthday of Queen Elizabeth the Queen Mother was celebrated in many ways, one being a military parade by, among other units, the Household Cavalry and the Queen's Dragoon Guards. Why were an Aberdeen Angus bull, six chickens and a pack of dachshunds included in the parade?

146 (20/6/90) What did a metal-detecting enthusiast find in a field near Docking, Norfolk, that archaeologists believe was hidden during Boudicca's Iceni rebellion against the Romans in AD 60?

147 (21/6/90) Members of the Scotland Yard anti-terrorist squad defused an incendiary device sent by letter to which MP?

148 (22/6/90) What was the purpose of the Calcutt Committee and what did its report recommend?

149 (22/6/90) According to Relate, formerly the National Guidance Council, British taxpayers faced an annual bill of £1.3 billion because of what nature of domestic problem?

150 (23/6/90) Alan Williams, Labour MP for Swansea West, complained about the bill for Mrs Thatcher's official overseas visits since she came to power in 1979. What has been the cost to the taxpayer over these years, during which she has visited 54 different countries?

126 The admission on a large scale of mature and external part-time students. The university's Department of External Studies will be elevated this week to the same status as its 41 colleges and private halls.

127 Michael and Emma respectively, the former being favoured by 51 per cent of parents, the latter by 59 per cent. Least favourite for boys was Wilfred (4 per cent) and, for girls, Clementine, Edith, Enid and Olive, all of which scored 6 per cent.

128 RMS *St Helena Island*, which has regularly made an eight-week run (including a call at Cape Town on her return journey) to the island

129 The Ludgate Hill bridge, which had drawn an ugly line across the cathedral when viewed from the west.

130 Farmers and doctors. More than 4750 people commit suicide in Great Britain every year, or one every two hours, according to the report.

131 The regiment is only 30 soldiers below full establishment strength of 630, but officers are concerned that recruiting is maintained.

132 The Princess Royal. Her visit of 13 days was seen as a move to heal the rift between Great Britain and the Soviet Union since the murder of Tsar Nicholas II and his family.

133 The procession was at Walsingham, Norfolk, which for many centuries was an important place of pilgrimage.

134 Eton College, where she attended the ceremony in memory of its original charter given by Henry VI in 1440.

135 Medina at Newport, the county town of the Isle of Wight. Some 3800 people were summoned to appear before magistrates for failing to pay the tax; by 31 May, however, 1800 of those summoned had belatedly paid their due or instalments on it.

136 In an unprecedented challenge to the House of Commons, the Lords voted by 207 to 74, after lengthy debate, to throw out the Government's War Crimes Bill.

137 West Green House in Hartley Wintney, Hampshire. The isolated Queen Anne mansion may now have to be demolished.

138 Barbara Castle, the former Labour cabinet minister; Dame Lydia Dunn, who has been prominent in trying to safeguard the interests of Hong Kong residents after the colony is returned to China in 1997; Sir Robert Haslam, chairman of British Coal; Sir Peter Lane, chairman of the executive committee of the National Union of Conservative Associations; Sir George Porter, president of the Royal Society, and Dr Robert Runcie, the Archbishop of Canterbury, who is shortly to retire and is already a Lord spiritual.

139 Michael Spicer, the housing minister, announced the spending of several million pounds to provide clean but simple living quarters in a variety of buildings, including church halls and former hospitals.

140 Barristers specialising in commercial work earn the greater fee, while those specialising in criminal work are less handsomely rewarded.

141 Its classics faculty. Classics has been taught at Cambridge for six centuries. Oxford University is shortly to follow suit.

142 Following the upheavals in eastern Europe, Great Britain's defence needs were reviewed. Orders for 33 Tornado aircraft were cancelled as one step in securing savings of more than £600 million to keep the defence ministry within its £21.2 billion budget for this year.

143 Eight pillows, to be made to the same specification as those he gave to the Prince as a wedding gift in 1981.

144 Lavinia, Duchess of Norfolk.

145 They represented more than 300 organisations of which the Queen Mother is patron or president.

146 A hoard of 153 Iron Age silver coins. Cleaning exposed the inscriptions ECE and ECEN, which may refer to tribal names, and ANTD and SAENU, which could refer to tribal leaders.

147 Nicholas Bennett, Conservative member for Pembroke.

148 The committee was set up in April 1989 to investigate press invasion of privacy. In effect, Great Britain's newspaper industry, particularly the tabloids, were given a 12-month deadline to 'put its house in order' or face harsh statutory controls.

149 In the period 1987/88, the last for which accurate figures are available, the Government spent £3.5 million a day on social security benefits and other payments to divorced and separated people.

150 A parliamentary answer revealed that £4.3 million had been spent on overseas travel by the Prime Minister and her staff, Mrs Thatcher travelling more frugally than virtually any other world leader.

151 (26/6/90) Where in London were eight people, including a peer and three American tourists, injured on 25 June by the explosion of a terrorist bomb?

152 (26/6/90) According to a survey organised jointly by the Audit Commission and the Institution of Environmental Health Officers, what percentage of food premises in England and Wales present a high health risk?

153 (26/6/90) What power of dismissal by local authorities over school governors did Lord Justice Leggatt uphold in a test case in the High Court?

154 (2/7/90) A police officer, called to an incident at Aylesford, Kent, was attacked by a Rottweiler, which bit his right hand before grasping the other in its jaws. The officer escaped further injury only by strangling the dog. How did he manage this?

155 (2/7/90) For what purpose did Cecil Parkinson, the transport secretary, invite the father of a victim of the Lockerbie air disaster to meet his officials?

156 (4/7/90) Which English road is to be up-graded to a six-lane motorway, the work to be completed by the year 2000?

157 (4/7/90) Which famous mount in the royal stables died, at the Royal Mews, Windsor Castle?

158 (5/7/90) According to the latest figures from the Office of Population Censuses and Surveys, Great Britain's ethnic minority community now numbers how many, forming what per cent of the population?

159 (5/7/90) For what purpose did water companies plan to charge £200, pre-paid, to most householders by the year 2000?

160 (5/7/90) A random survey of 38 district, metropolitan and London councils, found that what per cent of eligible adults had made at least some payment towards their Community Charge bills?

161 (6/7/90) Members of the House of Lords defeated the Government by how many votes in a division concerning which type of pet?

162 (6/7/90) An appeal was launched to raise money for what village cemetery and why was this necessary?

163 (9/7/90) What is unique about Great Britain's Golden Promise beer, launched today?

164 (9/7/90) What was the purpose of the first national enquiry, to last three years at an

estimated cost of £750,000 and entitled 'The Third Age'?

165 (10/7/90) What is the purpose of a network called 'family hearing centres', plans for which were announced by the Lord Chancellor?

166 (12/7/90) What encroachment of the Government's privatisation policy was announced by the Home Office concerning the criminal justice system?

167 (16/7/90) What effect will the implementation of the European Community Spirit Drinks Regulation, to apply from 15 December, have on Scotch whiskies?

168 (17/7/90) Whom did the Liberal Democrats choose as their president from September in succession to Ian Wrigglesworth MP?

169 (17/7/90) To bring the United Kingdom into line with the rest of the European Community, what test, voluntary from September but probably compulsory from 1992, was introduced for learner drivers?

170 (20/7/90) What measure did police chief constables advocate to facilitate detection of nationwide crime?

171 (21/7/90) What was unusual about the burial of Sophia Elizabeth Wykeham, Baroness Wenman, at Thame Park, Oxfordshire?

172 (24/7/90) Which British minister became the first to visit China since the Tiananmen Square massacre in 1989?

173 (25/7/90) Who, wearing dark glasses, assumed the name Arthur Fenn, for what purpose and where?

174 (26/7/90) The Rt Rev George Carey was chosen to succeed Dr Robert Runcie as Archbishop of Canterbury. Aged 54, he will be the youngest archbishop in recent history. In what other ways is he distinguished from his immediate predecessors?

175 (26/7/90) The Government announced that the three armed services were to be reduced in strength, mainly through natural wastage, now that conflict with the Eastern bloc is less likely. By what number of servicemen will each arm be cut?

151 At the Carlton Club in the West End of London. The IRA bomb, of between 10lb and 15lb, caused extensive damage to the club, which is a bastion of traditional Tory values.

152 One in eight, and one in 25 should be prosecuted or closed down. 'Takeaways' are the worst offenders, one in five being judged 'a significant health risk'.

153 Local authorities are entitled to appoint governors in direct proportion to their political make-up; thus political parties that gain control of local authorities are entitled to dismiss school governors, earlier appointed by their political rivals, and nominate their own.

154 By slipping his truncheon under the dog's collar and twisting it to make it release its grip, hopefully without killing it. Other policemen had to prize open the dead dog's jaws to free the officer.

155 Jim Swire, a leader of the United Kingdom Families Group, whose daughter died in the disaster, claimed that he had taken a fake Semtex bomb in a radio cassette recorder, similar to the one used to conceal the explosive device that destroyed Pan-Am flight 103 over Lockerbie 18 months ago, through a special security check at Heathrow airport and on to a flight to the United States to test security.

156 The Great North Road. The entire 200-mile length of the A1 between the M25 London orbital road and Tyneside will be enlarged in two stages.

157 *Burmese*, which the Queen rode at many ceremonies, including Trooping the Colour.

158 2.58 million, or nearly five per cent of the country's population. The survey of the years 1981 to 1988 indicate that the minority population is increasing at more than 80,000 a year.

159 Water meters.

160 More than three-quarters, an average of 75.8 per cent. The lowest recorded council was Camden (50 per cent paying the tax), the highest Poole, Dorset (96 per cent paying).

161 By 155 votes to 83, a majority of 72, the Lords backed a cross-party amendment to set up a dog register next year.

162 Parents of children killed in the 1966 Aberfan tip disaster in Wales, in which 116 children and 28 adults perished, found that the fund set up after the tragedy no longer produces sufficient income to care for the graves.

163 The beer, developed by Caledonian Breweries of Edinburgh, is made by using barley and hops from Great Britain and Tasmania, grown without the use of chemicals and pesticides.

164 A study into the lifestyle and work opportunities for the 14 million active and healthy United Kingdom citizens between the ages of 50 and 75 to see how they could still make themselves useful to others.

165 Ninety-four centres in England and Wales will be established where, for the first time, children's cases will be handled by specially trained judges.

166 The running of a new remand centre and prisoner escort duties will be put out to tender. The department claimed that the move would substantially reduce the £80 million annual cost of ferrying prisoners to and from courts.

167 From that date all Scotch whiskies must be bottled at a strength of not less than 40 per cent by volume, thus distinguishing them from below-strength brands bearing Scottish names.

168 Charles Kennedy, aged 30, MP for Ross, Cromarty and Skye.

169 Written tests with 100 questions, which will be closely monitored by the transport department before they are made mandatory.

170 They proposed that a powerful police overlord should be appointed to control a new national criminal intelligence service and for five super regional crime squads to be established.

171 The baroness, born in 1790, died in 1870. So terrified was she of being buried alive that she left instructions in her will that her corpse be placed in an oak coffin with a breathing dome at its head in case physicians had been premature in pronouncing her dead.

172 Francis Maude, minister of state at the Foreign Office; on the day of his departure it was announced that, on his return, he will become financial secretary at the Treasury following a cabinet reshuffle.

173 Arthur Scargill, president of the NUM, assumed the name at Leeds/Bradford airport when about to fly to Paris to discuss charges concerning allegations of financial malpractice.

174 The son of a hospital porter, Dr Carey is a true cockney, born within the sound of Bow bells, and left school at 15.

175 The army by 40,000, the RAF by 14,000 and the navy by 3000.

176 (28/7/90) In what way did the Queen make history in the Solent?

177 (30/7/90) In what way will the legal profession's machinery for handling complaints from the public be subject to close scrutiny in the near future?

178 (30/7/90) The occupants of which London nightclub were held at gunpoint by a Syrian for 10 hours before his arrest released them?

179 (2/8/90) In what way did the term 'signed, sealed and delivered' cease to apply in respect of legal and other documents and deeds?

180 (4/8/90) What development at Oxford, one of the dearest wishes of Cardinal John Henry Newman, is to be realised a hundred years after his death?

181 (8/8/90) According to a review of population trends in Europe, in *Lloyd's Log*, the magazine for Lloyd's of London, what percentage of people will be a pensioner and what percentage over 75 by the year 2040?

182 (8/8/90) What is the purpose of a trust fund, set up by his friends in memory of Ian Gow, the Conservative MP murdered by the IRA?

183 (11/8/90) Why was a three-year-old Border Lakeland terrier called Bob, the aggrieved party in a dispute, refused bail by magistrates at Keighley, West Yorkshire?

184 (13/8/90) At which resort in the United Kingdom did the local council install surveillance cameras on the seafront and for what purpose?

185 (14/8/90) Which politician called for a truce in his party's attacks on which party and why?

186 (15/8/90) On what grounds did a nun, Sister Carmel Bateson, of the Association of the Holy Family of Bordeaux, win a test case against her local authority in West Yorkshire, over her obligation to pay the Community Charge?

187 (16/8/90) Which department at the House of Commons has accumulated a cash mountain of more than £2 million and how?

188 (28/8/90) The 'Guinness Case', the most expensive in British legal history, was estimated to have cost how much?

189 (29/8/90) A record fine was imposed at Southwark Crown Court on whom and by whom?

190 (29/8/90) What law came into effect on 28 August concerning computers?

191 (5/9/90) The centre of which Elizabethan market town was destroyed by fire yesterday?

192 (6/9/90) How many Labour MPs died this year, up to September? Who was the last and what was his Parliamentary seat?

193 (12/9/90) Heads of leading independent schools are to combine with state secondary school heads to monitor what?

194 (12/9/90) Which former Tory MP was selected as prospective candidate for Eastbourne, following the murder of Ian Gow by the IRA?

195 (12/9/90) Why were a Yorkshire terrier and a lurcher, owned by a Lincolnshire family, ordered to be destroyed, in the first case of its kind in seven years?

196 (13/9/90) What modification was announced by British Rail to the proposed Channel Tunnel rail link, designed to reduce the environmental impact of the project?

197 (14/9/90) The first of the series of Ovaltine narrowboats, which operated in the 1920s, was relaunched yesterday on the Grand Union Canal after restoration. To what purpose will it be put?

198 (15/9/90) How was the Sabbath of the presbyterians on the Outer Hebridean island of Lewis and Harris threatened?

199 (15/9/90) What was the purpose of the biggest flypast of military aircraft seen over London since the Coronation and of what did it consist?

200 (15/9/90) Charges against a doctor of misconduct, of which he was cleared, led to demands that the General Medical Council review its disciplinary procedures in what way?

176 The Queen and the Duke of Edinburgh, aboard the royal yacht *Britannia*, reviewed a flotilla gathered in the Solent to mark the 150th anniversary of the founding of Cunard. She later made history by becoming the first reigning monarch to sail on a liner (the *Queen Elizabeth II*) with other passengers, as the ship reached Southampton.

177 The Lord Chancellor, under his legal reform bill, will appoint the first legal services ombudsman for England and Wales in response to what he regards as 'public disquiet' under the present system, where complaints are dealt with by the Law Society and the Bar.

178 *Tokyo Joe*, in Clarges Street near Piccadilly. During the siege the gunman repeatedly threatened to blow up the club, which is much used by Arab businessmen.

179 The ancient phrase has become obsolete as a result of legislation which came into force on 1 August. Henceforth, legal deeds have to be signed, witnessed and delivered. Previously there was no legal requirement for witnesses.

180 The foundation of a Roman Catholic oratory as a centre of prayer and study. Newman, one of the founders of the Oxford Movement, was converted to Rome and always hoped to open a religious house in Oxford.

181 One in five Europeans will be a pensioner, one in 10 over 75.

182 To benefit young Northern Ireland people, so that the fund would represent 'the lasting triumph of good over evil'.

183 The dog had been savaged by a fox while hunting; application for bail was opposed by the RSPCA, which has had Bob in kennels for four months.

184 Bournemouth; sunbathers and holidaymakers, if detected in activity unacceptable to south-coast standards of decency, will be cautioned by recorded voice booms from loudspeakers.

185 Kenneth Baker, the Conservative Party chairman, called for a truce in his party's attacks on Labour because of the confrontation in the Gulf.

186 Sister Carmel earns a salary as a deputy head teacher.She claimed that she had no personal income since her wages were paid under a covenant to the Holy Family sisters. The council had claimed that she gave her income to the sisters by choice and that, for religious exemption, people had to be without income and savings and be dependent on an order.

187 The refreshment department; the surplus, which was boosted by profits of £289,000 last year, has grown over the last 10 years but there seem few firm plans of how best to dispose of it.

188 The case, which lasted 112 days, is thought to have cost in excess of £25 million. Court administration costs have been calculated at £26 for each minute of the court day.

189 Mr Justice Henry sentenced Gerald Ronson, the head of Heron International, to a year in prison, £440,000 costs and a fine of £5 million for his part in the 'Guinness Case'.

190 Computer hacking is now a crime, the act making it illegal to gain access to or modify computer material without authority.

191 Totnes, in Devon; the town's centrepiece, the East Gate, was reduced to bare stones.

192 Allen Adams, the member for Paisley North, aged only 44, became the fifth Labour member to die. The others likewise were middle-aged: Pat Wall, 57; Mike Carr, 43; Sean Hughes, 44, and Allan Roberts, 43.

193 Teacher quality: the survey has been commissioned by the Headmaster's Conference, the Girls' Schools Association and the Secondary Heads Association, to measure the quality of teachers entering schools.

194 Richard Hickmet, aged 42, Tory member for Glanford and Scunthorpe from 1983 to 1987.

195 The two dogs had been imported from Zambia, the terrier having been found as a stray. One of the dogs was discovered to have rabies and was thought to have had a fight with the other while in quarantine kennels.

196 British Rail propose a half-mile, 60ft high viaduct to carry the link across the picturesque Boxley Valley, north of Maidstone.

197 The vessel will be fitted out for use as a classroom and conference centre by the charity Waterways Heritage.

198 Caledonian MacBrayne plans to start Sunday ferry sailings from Tarbert, on Harris, to Uig, Skye, next spring.

199 To commemorate the 50th anniversary of the Battle of Britain. Fifteen formations, each comprising up to 16 aircraft, took part.

200 The Medical Defence Union and the Medical Protection Society said that accused doctors' anonymity should be preserved unless there was a finding of guilt.

1 (4/1/90) In January it was alleged that some meat from the carcasses of cattle infected with 'mad cow' disease was still reaching supermarkets. By what initial letters is the disease commonly known, and what do these initials stand for?

2 (5/1/90) The Department of Health announced that it was allocating £1 million a year over the next three years to provide cochlear implants. What is their purpose?

3 (6/1/90) According to studies prepared for the Arthritis and Rheumatism Research Council, at any given time more than 10 per cent of adults experience discomfort in what part of the body?

4 (8/1/90) Professor Harold Edgerton, the inventor of a special photographic technique, died on 7 January. What is this technique? What is it used for?

5 (10/1/90) A fungus gnat that died more than 40 million years ago had been preserved in mineral amber. Some of its genetic code was in perfect condition. What prospect did this offer scientists?

6 (12/1/90) A new theory was advanced in the USA to explain why alcohol affects women faster than men. What is it?

7 (15/1/90) What new theory was advanced to account for the mysterious wartime flying accident in which the Duke of Kent, father of the present Duke, was killed in 1942?

8 (20/1/90) What eating habits were suggested in the *British Medical Journal* as being the key to a healthier diet?

9 (6/2/90) A Naumann's Thrush from Siberia was seen in the United Kingdom for the first time in February. It was thought to have been driven off course by strong winds. Where should it have been by that time of year?

10 (7/2/90) How and why did 79 beagle puppies die on a North Sea ferry?

11 (8/2/90) The brain of which distinguished Russian was sent to the Soviet Academy's Neurological Institute, and why?

12 (16/2/90) What new danger was discovered for air crews and passengers?

13 (16/2/90) Why did the Government order an urgent investigation of safety at nuclear power stations in February?

14 (21/2/90) In what way did American scientists propose to use high-temperature superconducting material in its first important commercial military application?

15 (7/3/90) What development by British engineers will, it is thought, relegate the familiar computer keyboard to the museum?

16 (10/3/90) Researchers at Utah State University and the University of Oklahoma discovered that certain molluscs change dramatically in what way when confronted with predators?

17 (12/3/90) Sir Robert Watson-Watt has always been credited with the development for practical use of radar, the system that proved crucial in defending the British Isles during the Battle of Britain. New research, however, unearthed patents belonging to whom that date back to 1926, nine years previously?

18 (13/3/90) What new method of generating electricity would, it was announced, be demonstrated later in the year?

19 (13/3/90) Scientists claimed to have discovered a Rhabdodon. What is it?

20 (14/3/90) The Nature Conservancy Council announced the demise of which member of the ladybird family?

21 (6/4/90) What was extraordinary about Lyme Regis fisherman Mr John Wason's catch?

22 (9/4/90) What tiny, British-designed jet, powered by engines at first meant for use in cruise missiles, may revolutionize private and business flying?

23 (14/4/90) In what way did the National Rivers Authority try to inhibit the growth of the blue-green algae which contamined 25 lakes and reservoirs during the summer of 1989, poisoning sheep, dogs and other creatures?

24 (19/4/90) Which British island, contaminated with anthrax as an experiment in biological warfare during the Second World War, was returned to its owners after years of testing and decontamination?

25 (19/4/90) In what way was the solitary lives of male gorillas in captivity made more bearable for them?

1 BSE, properly called Bovine Spongiforme Encephalopathy.

2 Bionic implants to provide hearing aids for the totally deaf.

3 The neck.

4 Ultra high-speed strobe photography. It enables fast-moving objects, such as bullets and the wings of humming birds, to be 'stopped' in flight.

5 That they might resurrect the insect—and possibly, in coming years, other creatures, including dinosaurs.

6 Male stomachs contain more of an enzyme that breaks down alcohol before it enters the bloodstream.

7 A wrong setting on the flying boat's gyro-magnetic compass, then a new piece of equipment.

8 Research suggests that eating little and often seems to produce lower cholesterol levels.

9 The thrush is usually in China, Korea, Japan or Taiwan at this time of year.

10 They suffocated after their breeder locked the rear door of the lorry in which they were travelling to prevent anyone seeing them. They were destined for laboratory experiments in Scandinavia. The breeder was fined £5500 and the company that traded the dogs was fined £11,000 after admitting two similar offences.

11 That of Dr. Andrei Sakharov, Nobel-prize winner and human rights campaigner, to assist in a study of how gifted people think and behave.

12 On certain routes and at high altitudes, they are exposed to more radiation than most workers at nuclear plants. Flying at 40,000 feet over the North Pole, for example, produces a 1.4 millirems level of radiation an hour, but only 0.4 millirems an hour at the same altitude over the Equator. Subsequently (20/2/90) the United States Government revised the figures, claiming that the danger was 17 times higher than estimated in the original report.

13 A report published by the University of Southampton found that men working in the plants might father children with leukemia.

14 The material will be used to make a microwave communications antenna on a military space craft, due to be launched in 1991.

15 A commercial, speech-activated computer, which can be operated even by people wholly without advanced computer language or technical knowledge.

16 Freshwater snails of the species *Physella virgata* double their normal size when they detect the presence of crayfish. The researchers think that the snails react to chemicals released by crayfish when they devour snails.

17 John Logie Baird, the father of television. Two independent researchers, Mr Tom McArthur and Mr Peter Waddell, unearthed a ministry file entitled *The Use of Television in Aircraft*, the contents of which detailed Baird's work.

18 The first wave power station, which it was thought could generate electricity as cheaply as hydro-electric power. The prototype power station is near Portnahaven on the Rinns of Islay, Strathclyde.

19 A dinosaur. Scientists claim that the newly discovered remains belong to a species of Rhabdodon—a two-legged, plant-eating reptile—up to 3.5 metres long and 1.5 metres tall that roamed the earth 65 to 68 million years ago. The fossils were found in Catalonia.

20 The 13-spotted ladybird. There are 42 other species of ladybird thriving in the United Kingdom, and why *hippodamia redecimpuncta* proved the exception is unknown.

21 Mr Wason netted a 20lb grouper fish; these are normally found off Australia, in the Mediterranean or other much warmer waters. Scientists believe its appearance may be further evidence of the greenhouse effect.

22 The four-seater mini executive jet, designed by Mr Ian Chichester-Miles. The aircraft, named the *Leopard*, will, it is hoped, go on sale for about £450,000 within the next three years. It will have a cruising altitude of some 50,000 feet, a range of more than 1700 miles and yet achieve 20 miles to the gallon.

23 By experimenting with the use of surplus harvest straw which, in bales, would be submerged in nets. Scientists have found some evidence to suggest that straw contains algae-inhibiting properties.

24 Gruinard, some half a mile off the north-west Scottish coast near the mouth of Little Loch Broom. It had been off-limits since its requisition by the Ministry of Supply in 1942.

25 As the male population of gorillas in captivity increases, the only alternative to the plight of bored, lone males seemed to be euthanasia. Now, however, it is proposed to keep them in bachelor groups, precisely in the manner many live in the wild.

26 (23/4/90) According to *Science* (vol 248, pp 206–8), new measurements made in the Swiss Alps provide the first evidence that thinning of the ozone layer is increasing levels of Ultraviolet-B radiation in Europe, heightening the risk of skin cancers and cataracts. By how much has radiation falling on the Swiss Alps increased during the past decade?

27 (25/4/90) What was the name and purpose of the object thrust into orbit 380 miles above earth, successfully launched at a second attempt?

28 (7/5/90) The Clore Foundation donated £1 million to the London Zoo to relaunch the Clore Pavilion in a bid to conserve what nature of creatures?

29 (9/5/90) What is the purpose of the Trafficmaster, a device which received its government operating licence today?

30 (10/5/90) France's high-speed TGV train broke its own world rail speed record with a run of what speed, according to an SNCF national railway spokesman?

31 (11/5/90) What creature, it was conjectured, might be the oldest living animal in Great Britain?

32 (16/5/90) What is the purpose of an artificial nose, produced by a research team at the University of Manchester's Institute of Science and Technology?

33 (17/5/90) To what peace-time purpose did the American Institute of Aeronautics and Astronautics propose that nuclear weapons should be put?

34 (19/5/90) The theory that the dinosaurs were eliminated by the impact on Earth of a massive asteroid or comet 65 million years ago was given greater credibility by the discovery of what?

35 (24/5/90) What was the cause of the fall in birthrate of the apes (correctly, Barbary macaques) of Gibraltar, where they have been established from the time of the Napoleonic Wars at least?

36 (1/6/90) Where in Britain was the Arivert Murrelet to be found this month, and what is it?

37 (7/6/90) Specimens of what British vegetation are to be blasted into space by America's National Aeronautics and Space Administration and for what purpose?

38 (16/6/90) Why did Vauxhall, the motor-car manufacturers, recall more than 29,000 cars from its top-selling Cavalier range?

39 (22/6/90) What development will enable inefficient cars that spew clouds of environmentally damaging gases from their exhaust pipes to be pinpointed from the roadside in seconds?

40 (23/6/90) A Juwardi was returned to Australia from Bedford University, where it had been for over a century. What is it?

41 (28/6/90) Which British scientific establishment, after 45 years of fruitless search for a cure for what ailment, was closed down at the end of June?

42 (29/6/90) What addition to the MoT test was proposed by Cecil Parkinson, the transport secretary?

43 (30/6/90) Why did NASA, the United States space agency, ground its entire shuttle fleet?

44 (3/7/90) In what way did European scientists achieve a world 'first' in space flight with the space probe *Giotto*?

45 (5/7/90) European airlines, telephone companies and electronics engineers are completing plans for what innovation in passenger flight?

46 (6/7/90) What problem came to light on the 10-mile Banbury extension to the M40, as yet unopened, that will cost up to £18 million to correct?

47 (6/7/90) Some assumptions about the origins and spread of the killer disease Aids were overturned by a report in *The Lancet*, when what was revealed?

48 (7/7/90) What new development helps to cure, or at least curb, painful migraine attacks without the need for drugs?

49 (7/7/90) Which engineering project, not yet complete, will be used by only four per cent of the travelling public on a regular basis, according to a survey by Kaliber Enterprise, an Oxford-based research company?

50 (9/7/90) Cecil Parkinson, transport secretary, ordered the re-examination of what disaster at sea and why?

26 About one per cent annually.

27 The Hubble Space Telescope which, at that altitude, will operate without interference from the atmosphere.

28 Rare, small mammals, such as the British dormouse, which is becoming scarce because of modern agricultural methods.

29 It is Great Britain's first in-car traffic information system that can alert drivers on road congestion,

30 The new record – 320mph, compared with the previous record of 302mph – was set on a TGV Atlantique track near Tours in central France.

31 A tortoise belonging to the 17th Earl of Devon, which is believed to be at least 140 years old.

32 To assess the quality of some of Great Britain's beers.

33 With the thaw in East–West relations, nuclear weapons should be redeployed to defend Earth against asteroids, which are sometimes wider than Great Britain and travel at some 46,000mph.

34 Researchers from the University of Arizona, examining geological features in the Colombian Basin, where North and South America join, have found what seems to be a crater, 180 miles wide, on the sea floor caused by an asteroid six-miles wide.

35 They had become addicted to sweets and other treats, liberally proferred by the three and a half million people who annually visit Gibraltar.

36 On Lundy Island; it is a 10-inch black, white and grey bird, a member of the Auk family, which has not previously been seen outside the Pacific.

37 Three hundred Thale Cress seeds, *Arabidopsis*, will be launched in December and subsequently brought back to Earth so that scientists can study how the seeds cope with darkness and the absence of the Earth's natural gravity.

38 As a precaution, after a driver was seriously injured when the seat belt of his three-day-old Cavalier failed when the car was involved in a collision.

39 A hand-held sensor that can detect the level of carbon monoxide and carbon dioxide coming from a vehicle, even at high speeds.

40 The remains of an Australian Aborigine, whose body was sent to Britain for experiments in the 19th century. Juwardi is an Aboriginal name for somebody whose spirit had not come to rest in its territory of origin.

41 The Common Cold Research Centre, near Salisbury, Wiltshire.

42 Strict exhaust emission standards. A badly tuned car uses more fuel, pumping out more CO_2 and toxic gases in consequence.

43 The discovery of a fuel leak in *Atlantis*, the second of its three craft, forced scientists to postpone a mission scheduled for next month.

44 Four years ago *Giotto* swept past the eye of Halley's Comet; the ship's systems were then put into 'hibernation' and, on 2 July, reactivated to catapult it out of the Earth's gravitational field to intercept Comet Grigg-Skjellerup 126 million miles away, in two years time.

45 An in-flight telephone service, which will put handsets on an initial 1000 passenger aircraft flying over western Europe.

46 Civil engineers found cracking in the surface.

47 A re-examination of patient records and tissue specimens by virologists at Manchester University medical schools showed that a former Royal Navy seaman, aged 25, died from the condition in the city in 1959, the case occurring 23 years earlier than any previously recorded.

48 Kaleidoscopic goggles, which pulse coloured lights into a patient's eyes.

49 The Eurotunnel; of the sample of 375 car passengers only four per cent said they would always use the tunnel and only 14 per cent said they would use it often.

50 A lengthy campaign on behalf of Captain Stanley Lord, of the *Californian*, who had long been held responsible for so many lives (1513) being lost when the *Titanic* struck an iceberg in 1912 on her maiden voyage and sank, the *Californian* being sufficiently near to offer more effective help. It has been claimed that Captain Lord was made a scapegoat for this and other failures which prevented more people being saved. The main evidence to be considered results from the discovery of the wreckage of the *Titanic* on the sea bed in 1985, which was found some distance from the predicted position and thus changes the *Californian*'s distance from her at the time of the incident.

51 (10/7/90) What health hazard will be posed by the expected influx of thousands of Hong Kong immigrants in the years prior to the colony's reverting to China in 1997?

52 (12/7/90) For what medical purpose were experts allowed to analyse small samples taken from human and monkey mummies in the British Museum?

53 (13/7/90) In an article published today in *Science*, an American team of scientists revealed that last autumn it had found, 95 miles southwest of Cairo in the Zeuglodon Valley, once part of the ancient Tethys Sea, the first known fossils of whales. The discovery, on analysis, confirmed what hitherto unsubstantiated belief?

54 (13/7/90) What discovery by researchers offered hope of new diagnostic tests and new treatments, the most important advance in years, for the control of neurofibromatsis?

55 (16/7/90) What human organs may it soon be possible for those willing to donate at death?

56 (16/7/90) Which species of bird was reintroduced into England at a secret location after its absence from these islands for the past 100 years?

57 (23/7/90) Why did scientists from Great Britain, West Germany, the USA and Japan, armed with sophisticated cameras and microphones, camp out at five sites on the Wiltshire Downs?

58 (24/7/90) What is novel in the way in which prostate gland surgery will shortly be performed on a number of patients?

59 (24/7/90) What outstanding attribute is claimed by Vickers Defence Systems for its new Challenger 2 tank?

60 (27/7/90) What new technique, according to *The Lancet*, has been developed in Australia that can tell the sex of an unborn child and also if it is carrying inherited disorders?

61 (27/7/90) The steep rise in base metal prices led the Royal Mint to plan what alteration in the coinage?

62 (28/7/90) What danger did biologists and environmentalists foresee in the increasing introduction of smoke detectors in homes, offices and factories?

63 (30/7/90) What safety fears were expressed by the chairman of the Association of Chief Police Officers at the Royal Society for the Prevention of Accidents concerning the Vauxhall Carlton Lotus, a new model due to be launched at the Birmingham Motorshow in September?

64 (31/7/90) William Bates, one of 21 regional finalists in the Year of the Invention Competition, invented what modification to the disposable syringe and in what way may this prove beneficial to human health?

65 (1/8/90) What piece of equipment, among other improvements in National Health ambulances, will be installed at a cost of £3.8 million and for what purpose?

66 (2/8/90) British researchers discovered a possible link between a pain-killing drug given during labour and a vitamin injection for newborn infants, seemingly causing an increased risk of what disease in childhood?

67 (4/8/90) Where in the United Kingdom on 3 August was what temperature recorded, the highest since when?

68 (8/8/80) Richard Lucy, a British inventor, devised what promising method, called perpetual power, to provide what service?

69 (8/8/90) Specialists at two London hospitals—Professor Gian Viberti, and colleagues at the United Medical Schools of Guy's and St Thomas's hospitals—found ways to detect early signs of what potentially fatal disease, opening prospects of its prevention?

70 (8/8/90) A sanctuary for what creatures and why was started at Walton Highway, Norfolk?

71 (9/8/90) According to Mintel, the market research analysts, a survey, claimed to be the most comprehensive yet, revealed that citizens of which major European country are least likely to drink alcohol regularly?

72 (11/8/90) What is the name of the American spacecraft that yesterday was successfully put into orbit around Venus and what is its purpose?

73 (13/8/90) By how much, according to researchers at Columbia University, New York, may Carbon 14 dating be inaccurate and why?

74 (14/8/90) Hoverspeed's SeaCat catamaran, the 200-tonne, 250ft twin-hulled craft, began services today between Portsmouth and Cherbourg. What advantages are claimed for this mode of Channel crossing?

75 (14/8/90) In what way may three British scientists have solved the mystery of how the salmon finds its way back across thousands of miles of ocean to the river where it was born?

51 Tuberculosis, which is up to 30 times more prevalent in Hong Kong than in Great Britain.

52 Following the discovery last week that the Aids virus killed a British seaman in 1959, 23 years before the first recorded case in Great Britain, two Dutch virologists will use the same analysis techniques to discover whether ancestors of the Aids virus were present as long ago as 3500 BC.

53 Firm evidence emerged that whales had hind legs and feet before they forsook the land for the sea some 50 million years ago.

54 Scientists identified the gene thought to be responsible for a form of the disease, an hitherto uncurable disorder of the central nervous system which affects some 20,000 people in Great Britain.

55 Ovaries, for use by infertile couples hoping for a child.

56 Eleven young red kites, imported from Spain, were released in an attempt to reintroduce the bird, which used to breed in much of Great Britain

57 To discover the cause of eight new mysterious circles of flattened grain in wheatfields.

58 The operation will be carried out by a robot, under a surgeon's supervision.

59 It has been demonstrated that its Chobham armour is tougher and stronger than any other system; during trials the armour has withstood every type of tank gun shell fired at it,

60 Doctors at Flinders University, Adelaide, used molecular biology techniques to isolate foetal cells from maternal blood and by analysing small amounts of DNA in the cells correctly identified the sex of the foetus.

61 Copper-plated versions of the 1p and 2p coins will be produced.

62 Smoke detectors, the installation of which is being encouraged, generally contain Americium 241, which can cause lung and liver cancer. The risk stems not from radiation in buildings, where it is minimal, but when they are discarded and replaced.

63 The executive car is said to be capable of 176mph, making it potentially lethal, especially in the hands of inexperienced drivers.

64 The disposable syringe can be used once only, since it has a thermoplastic rubber piston, part of which breaks off from flesh after use, making it no longer serviceable.

65 All 2350 emergency ambulances will be equipped with defibrillators to help save the lives of heart attack victims.

66 Cancer; the study of 16,000 children, born in the same week in 1970, showed that those whose mothers received the drug pethidine during labour and who themselves received vitamin K injections to prevent brain haemorrhaging, were three times more prone to cancer by the age of ten.

67 At Cheltenham, where 37.1°C (98.8°F) was recorded at 3pm, one degree above the previous recorded high set on 9 August 1911.

68 He may have developed a novel way of harnessing the tides to generate continuous and cheap electricity. The project uses water and air-filled buoys which, linked by pulleys to a rotary engine, will generate electricity both on the rising and falling tides. Present plants produce power on ebb tides only.

69 Diabetic kidney disease, which affects some 750,000 people in Great Britain and causes kidney failure in about 600 patients a year. The researchers found that 80 per cent of diabetics who develop kidney disease show a minute rise in albumin, a protein excreted in their urine, long before they become ill, and have higher than average blood pressure. Detecting these early signs would not only lead to the disease's prevention but would reduce the need for dialysis treatment and kidney transplantation.

70 Ferrets, many of whom are abandoned as pets.

71 Great Britain; more than a quarter of British adults claimed that they would not consume as much as one alcoholic drink a month.

72 America's *Magellan* spacecraft is to provide the first detailed maps of the planet's surface.

73 This widely used technique for assessing the age of ancient remains could be inaccurate, they claimed, by as much as 3500 years because of fluctuations in the amounts of Carbon 14 produced in ancient atmospheres, which in turn causes an imbalance of isotopes in remains, a balance crucial to the workings of the carbon dating method.

74 Capable of carrying 450 passengers and 80 cars, the vessel can make the Channel crossing in about two hours, 40 minutes.

75 The scientists detected the presence of magnetic particles in the brain and along the lateral line of the Atlantic salmon. They think that the salmon use these particles of magnetite to detect and follow the Earth's magnetic field.

76 (15/8/90) What is the purpose of the new technique called gas chromatography?

77 (17/8/90) In what way, after 66 years, did the Forestry Commission concede that nature knows best, in the first instance in respect of the Forest of Dean?

78 (20/8/90) A trainee horticulturist accidentally unearthed in Yorkshire which of the world's rarest gourmet foods?

79 (21/8/90) Why did British Telecom refuse to service telephone lines on two south London housing estates, the Gloucester Grove and North Peckham estates?

80 (21/8/90) In what way, according to Plymouth Marine Laboratory, might iron, if scattered on the sea's surface, slow down global warming?

81 (21/8/90) Some people in Camelford, Cornwall, who drank water contaminated by aluminium sulphate, accidentally discharged into the River Camel two years ago, were found to be suffering from what physical malady?

82 (22/8/90) Why do some scientists think that salmonella, the bane of the food industry, might emerge as a potential life-saver?

83 (23/8/90) According to results of an 11-year study published by British specialists in the *New England Journal of Medicine*, babies exposed to house dust are at extra risk of what disorder in later life?

84 (24/8/90) What are 'neutral networks' and what breakthrough was achieved by British Telecom's research into them?

85 (25/8/90) In 1988, water supplies to Camelford, north Cornwall, were found to be contaminated with aluminium sulphate; where were levels of aluminium nine times the EC limit found in tap water in March 1990, a fact disclosed this August?

86 (25/8/90) Which breed of cat, deemed extinct by the American Cat Fanciers' Association since about the middle of this century, is now being successfully bred in this country, and what are its characteristics?

87 (29/8/90) What was the genetic engineering purpose of impregnating a Norfolk potato crop with a gene taken from peas?

88 (30/8/90) What is Electrostatic Document Analysis (ESDA)?

89 (15/8/90) NASA released a photograph from the Hubble space telescope, which showed what concerning 30 Doradus?

90 (16/8/90) Why were executives of the Ford motor company called before a parliamentary inquiry?

91 (16/8/90) What bird, found on the river Weaver in Cheshire, caused ornithologists to flock to the area and why?

92 (21/8/90) What correlation existed, it was suggested by Bernadette Modell, a scientist at University College, London, between short-sightedness in young children and their IQ?

93 (24/8/90) Why did British Airways last night ground its fleet of new Boeing 767 twin-jet airliners?

94 (1/9/90) August 1990 was the hottest in Great Britain since scientific records began in which year?

95 (6/9/90) Where, in an announcement today by John Wakeham, the energy secretary, is it proposed to build Great Britain's next nuclear power station?

96 (10/9/90) How have at least three British judges altered their way of taking notes during court cases?

97 (12/9/90) Why may video rental shops in Great Britain have become a thing of the past by the end of 1991?

98 (15/9/90) Why has a rare marine creature, Ivell's anemone, disappeared from the south coast of Britain, its only known habitat?

99 (15/9/90) What simple error wrecked the $1.5 billion (£802 million) Hubble space telescope's focus?

100 (15/9/90) Why were exotic natural specimens, including sub-species of the venomous black widow spider, a huge collection of ferocious-looking beetles, among much else, sent through the postal system from a refrigerator in Manchester to scientists at the Natural History Museum in London?

76 A 'fingerprinting' technique, used by Dutch authorities, to analyse samples of crude oil shipped into Rotterdam. The technique is being employed to identify Iraqi or Kuwaiti crude oil smuggled in.

77 The forest, enclosed by the valleys of the Severn and the Wye, has been overexploited during the centuries, its oaks used in the building of medieval castles, cathedrals, manor houses and ships, and during the early years of the Industrial Revolution to help fire the furnaces. The commission conceded that natural regeneration of trees provided greater density and more timber than trees planted by man.

78 David Hollingsworth, a second-year student at Bishop Burton college, uncovered a 20-gram (0.7oz) white truffle.

79 Because, it was claimed, conditions in the crawlways represented an unacceptable risk to health and safety, risks arising from asbestos, electrical hazards, inadequate and vandalised lighting, broken glass and contamination with rat faeces and urine.

80 The theory, to be tested in the next few years, suggests that iron scattered across the southern oceans would encourage the growth of algae, which would capture carbon released into the atmosphere. Some of the algae would sink carrying the carbon with it.

81 Their toenails are growing deformed or falling out, allegedly the first sign of long-term damage from the poisoning. Several thousand people are thought to have drunk the contaminated water.

82 Scientists have discovered that the bacterium seems an ideal vehicle for new vaccines against such diseases as malaria, tetanus, typhoid and perhaps Aids.

83 Asthma; the researchers also say that an infant is more prone to the condition if either parent has asthma or hay fever.

84 A new class of computers, designed on principles similar to those of the human brain. They had been taught to recognise spoken words, carry out basic translations from English into French, and determine whether a sequence in English is grammatically constructed.

85 At St Minver, ten miles from Camelford. South West Water said that a burst main was to blame for the concentration of metals

86 The Maine coon, which can weigh 20lb, stand 12in at the shoulder, has a front paw span of 2in and measure 36in from whisker to tail.

87 It is hoped that the gene will make potatoes resistant to the Colorado beetle and the tuber moth, common pests of the potato.

88 It detects the indentations made in successive sheets of paper when the top sheet is written on.

89 The star-forming area known as 30 Doradus was found to have 60 stars in an area thought to have a single star.

90 To justify their use, when recruiting staff, of information on alleged subversives held by the Economic League.

91 A solitary long-billed dowitcher, which had been blown far off course across the Atlantic.

92 The difference between shortsighted children below the the age of 10 and other children, it was claimed, showed that the former could be as much as five to 10 points higher on the IQ scale.

93 Cracks were found in the pylons connecting the engines to the wings.

94 1659; central London experienced a mean temperature of 18.8C (65.84F), slightly higher than that of 1975, one of the previous warmer Augusts.

95 At Hinkley Point, Somerset.

96 They now type their notes into a personal computer on the bench.

97 An American entrepeneur proposes to beam an unlimited selection of films, television programmes and data direct to viewers' home recorders by satellite. Subscribers, equipped with new-generation video recorders, will tap into an electronic library over a free telephone line.

98 Because, it is thought, of hot summers and mild winters in recent years.

99 NASA investigators concluded that a 2ft metal rod, used in a measuring device which reads the curve of the mirror's surface as it is polished, was accidentally put in upside-down.

100 The consignments are just some of the fruits of Great Britain's first scientific expedition to Mongolia, undertaken by four students from Bristol university.

1 (16/3/90) What are these newly hatched fish, bringing to about 60 their total number in captivity, and how was the species brought near to extinction?

2 (17/3/90) A high-speed 'wingsail' trimaran is seen undergoing trials at Plymouth Sound in preparation for a world-wide launch. In what way is its design revolutionary and how will it make yachting an accessible sport to inexperienced land-lubbers?

3 (21/3/90) A duck, believed to be one of the world's rarest breed, lands at the Wildfowl and Wetlands Trust in Slimbridge, Gloucestershire. What is the name of its breed, how many remain in the wild and where is its natural habitat?

4 (15/5/90) What was notable about this wedding dress?

5 (1/6/90) Professor Ken Pounds of Leicester University is seen holding a model of what device, designed for what purpose?

6 (10/7/90) 'Ollie', a wooden owl, is employed by his 'handler' for what purpose?

1 *Haplochromis pyrrhocephalus*; these tiny fish have been the main sufferers from the colonization of Lake Victoria by voracious Nile perch, which escaped from fish farms some 40 years ago. Before the perch, there were 300 varieties of *Haplochromis* in the lake, but it was estimated last year that almost two thirds are now extinct in the wild.

2 The design of the 30ft *Zefyr* enables it to reverse and make three-point turns. Instead of rigging and sails, the vessel is fitted with an aircraft-style wing that is moved by computer to take best advantage of wind direction and force. Power is delivered to the wing's motor by solar cells housed at the ship's apex.

3 A white-winged wood duck; 200 pairs, it is thought, survive in the Far East. The species used to be found throughout South-east Asia but now only small groups exist in parts of north-east India, Sumatra, Thailand, Vietnam and Bangladesh. The duck weights up to three kilograms, double the size of a mallard.

4 The dress, made of platinum, was shown by Johnson Matthey, the precious metals group, to launch *Platinum 1990*, its annual review of the industry. Super-thin platinum was lined with Japanese paper and then shredded to a width of 0.33mm for weaving. The dress was valued at £300,000, and is modelled here flanked by security guards.

5 A telescope, which he helped to conceive, that will detect the 'light' generated by stars, giving a new insight on the universe. The telescope will be launched into orbit from Cape Canaveral.

6 To scare away pigeons from British Telecom's Madley satellite earth station near Hereford. The owl, costing about £4, is regarded as a cheap solution to an expensive cleaning problem caused by perching pigeons fouling the antennas.

1 (4/1/90) On 3 January, share prices rose to their highest level thus far on the London stock market. At what figure did the FT-SE index close?

2 (6/1/90) Which Australian businessman, with debts of $Aus 6 billion (almost £3 billion), began talks with a Singapore company about the sale of a controlling interest in his own company?

3 (10/1/90) Living costs in Argentina continued to soar, taking the inflation level for 1989 to the record-breaking peak of what annual per cent?

4 (11/1/90) Which company paid an estimated £1 billion for control of the once high-flying West German computer maker, Nixdorf?

5 (12/1/90) Eurotunnel confirmed that the funding crisis, which might have halted work on the project, was over. How was this achieved?

6 (19/1/90) Which bank bought Yorkshire Bank for £976.5 million?

7 (24/1/90) What business did General Electric Company buy for £310 million?

8 (25/1/90) Ford workers rejected union demands for a national strike over pay and accepted a two-year deal. What percentage increase was agreed for 1990?

9 (2/2/90) Nigel Lawson, after his resignation as Chancellor of the Exchequer, was offered, and accepted, what job for an estimated yearly salary of between £100,000 and £200,000.

10 (14/2/90) Which four leading City figures went on trial, accused of mounting an illegal share support scheme to bolster the Guinness share price during its takeover in 1986 of the Scottish drinks group, Distillers?

11 (15/2/90) To what level did the Abbey National, Great Britain's second biggest mortgage lender, raise its rate, the highest ever until then, on 14 January?

12 (15/2/90) Of what charge were Great Britain's leading oil companies cleared in respect of the price of petrol?

13 (24/2/90) What induced more than 600,000 Lloyds Bank Access customers, a fifth of the total and double the company's estimate, to destroy their credit cards?

14 (1/3/90) How many of the 5.5 million people who took part in the Abbey National flotation in July 1989 had sold their shares by March 1990?

15 (14/3/90) The Saatchi brothers, Maurice and Charles, under pressure from shareholders because of sliding profits from their advertising, agreed to a 30 per cent cut in their annual salaries. How much was this cut for each a year?

16 (16/3/90) Unemployment fell in February by what figure, making it the smallest drop since the number of jobless peaked in the summer of 1986?

17 (19/3/90) In what way did French authorities decree that the language of the Bourse should be amended?

18 (24/3/90) Why did Mr Ron Todd, the general secretary of the Transport and General Workers' Union, ask for an investigation into his union's affairs by the Serious Crime Squad?

19 (24/3/90) Why did the Department of Education and Science plan to pay Saatchi and Saatchi, the advertising agency, £2.2 million?

20 (24/3/90) Rising interest rates and dwindling income obliged which charity, with estimated debts of £2 million, to be voluntarily wound up?

21 (27/3/90) Mr Tony Baldry, the Under Secretary of State for Energy, announced the achievement of what percentage increase in productivity in the Nottinghamshire coalfield since 1985–6?

22 (27/3/90) Why did Ford plan to reduce by 8500 the number of assembly-line workers at its Halewood plant on Merseyside?

23 (28/3/90) What percentage pay rise, effective from January 1991, was awarded to 33,000 workers in the electrical contracting industry, thus giving them the highest base rate in the construction industry?

24 (28/3/90) The Prudential Corporation, Great Britain's largest insurer, announced pre-tax profits of £386 million, a nine per cent increase. In what area, however, did they suffer a £49 million loss?

25 (30/3/90) Mr Tiny Rowland, Lonrho chief executive, was given a salary rise of 30%, bringing his income to what annual figure?

1 2463.7.

2 Alan Bond, head of Bond Corp Holdings.

3 5000 per cent.

4 Siemens, the electronics group.

5 The 208 members of the banking consortium supporting the project made available up to £400 million to enable work to continue.

6 National Australia Bank.

7 The defence systems business of Ferranti International.

8 10.2 per cent, more than the inflation figure, and above Government guidelines.

9 He was appointed a part-time, non-executive director of Barclays Bank.

10 Ernest Saunders, the former chief executive of Guinness, Gerald Ronson, Chairman of Heron Corporation, Anthony Parnes, a City stockbroker, and Sir Jack Lyons, a millionaire financier.

11 15.4%.

12 They had been accused of operating a cartel to fix the price of petrol.

13 The bank's decision to charge an annual fee of £12. The figure was announced at the same time as was the company's losses for 1989 of £715 million, after a £1.8 billion provision against Third World loans. Profits from its credit card division had fallen by two-thirds to £11 million.

14 1.4 million, over a quarter.

15 They took an annual cut in salary of £187,000.

16 By a seasonally-adjusted 2000, bringing the total down to 1,610,000.

17 *Franglais*, Anglo-French terms such as 'venture capital', 'debt equity swaps' and 'blue chip', were to be outlawed to preserve the purity of the French language.

18 He had ordered a re-run of the elections for the national executive committee when evidence emerged that up to 2500 stolen voting papers in the union's first full postal ballot had been cast for left-wing candidates in marginal seats.

19 To pay for what is intended to be the biggest national teacher recruitment campaign ever mounted, since estimates suggest that shortage of teachers in key subjects will reach 18,200 by the middle of the decade.

20 War on Want, which had been founded 38 years ago to combat world poverty. The charity's demise came after numerous crises amid allegations of financial mismanagement, left-wing bias and a spate of resignations.

21 Sixty per cent, from 2.9 tonnes a man-shift in 1985–6 to 4.64 tonnes in the first 11 months of 1989–90. Nottinghamshire coalfield workers are affiliated to the Union of Democratic Mineworkers.

22 The cut, about a third of the total force, was part of a drive to reduce costs at Ford's 21 United Kingdom plants to meet Japanese competition. The Halewood plant, Ford's second largest in Great Britain, will achieve this reduction over the next five years by natural wastage and voluntary redundancies.

23 Twelve per cent, giving electricians a base rate of £5.50 an hour.

24 From their estage agency section.

25 His salary rises from £1 million to £1.3 million.

26 (31/3/90) What leisure interest did Pearson, the publishing, investment banking and oil services group, pay £60 million to acquire?

27 (3/4/90) By how much did panic selling send share prices crashing in the Tokyo Stock Exchange?

28 (10/4/90) Why did Ford cancel a £225 million investment in South Wales, that would have concentrated 70 per cent of its European engine production in Great Britain?

29 (10/4/90) Why was an inquiry ordered into the £550 million 'instant coffee' market?

30 (24/4/90) What financial arrangement, as a preliminary towards German reunification, did the West German Chancellor, Herr Helmut Kohl, take in respect of the two countries' currencies?

31 (2/5/90) According to a survey by *Personnel Today,* Junior office staff are happy to take as much holiday time as permissable, yet 8 out of 10 bosses do not take their full entitlement. What were the two main reasons given for this reluctance?

32 (7/5/90) London will be the location for the proposed new European Bank for Reconstruction and Development (EBRD). What will be its primary function?

33 (19/5/90) What reason did four Japanese companies give for halting exports of steel pipes and machinery to Moscow?

34 (31/5/90) What is Taurus and why is it estimated that it will cause the loss of between 2000 and 3000 jobs in the City by the end of 1993?

35 (20/6/90) Which British company beat 200 others to win a contract to build 1000 electric cars for Los Angeles, a city with some of the most stringent exhaust emission regulations in the world?

36 (21/6/90) What radical new plan was proposed by the Chancellor of the Exchequer, John Major, regarding European currency?

37 (21/6/90) The opening of the Green Show, the United Kingdom's biggest exhibition for companies and organisations committed to protecting the environment, was marred by objections to the presence of what organisation? What were the objections raised by other exhibitors and those companies which had declined to participate on this account?

38 (23/6/90) What did the Chancellor of the Exchequer, John Major, tell the Conservative Women's Conference in London that the Government would do if 'loan sharks', banks, building societies and credit card companies did not moderate their credit advertising?

39 (25/6/90) Which Labour-run council planned to play a part in the lucrative private enterprise market which annually surrounds which sporting event?

40 (25/6/90) Which company producing single malt Scotch whisky plans to double its production capacity in a £5 million development at its distillery at Tain, Ross and Cromarty?

41 (29/6/90) What are *sokaiya*?

42 (30/6/90) Fifty heavily guarded trucks under helicopter escort took what from West to East Germany, in preparation for the two country's eventual union?

43 (3/7/90) The executive chairman of which company, less than three years after its launch and having spent £250 million to date and probably incurring future losses of £70 to £100 million, claimed that it would start making a profit by the end of 1991?

44 (3/7/90) Where did the World Bank open its first office in Eastern Europe and why?

45 (7/7/90) What agreement signed by British Airways constituted the biggest single aircraft order ever placed by a British airline?

46 (10/7/90) Why did Legal & General sell Victory, Great Britain's second largest reinsurance company, to Nederlandse Reassurantie Groep and for how much?

47 (10/7/90) What did the Swiss Banking Commission move to abolish concerning customers' accounts?

48 (11/7/90) Which estate agency announced that it is to close 175 of its branches and why?

49 (13/7/90) Which British coins cost more to mint than their face value, according to an investigation into the working of the Royal Mint's annual coin sales?

50 (26/7/90) Which company signed a five-year exclusive contract valued at $5 billion with the Soviet Union to market and sell rough diamonds?

26 Alton Towers, the Midlands theme park.

27 The Nikkei index dived 1,978.38 points to close at 28,002.07, a collapse surpassed only by the 3,836-point fall on 'Black Monday' in October 1987.

28 According to the Secretary of State for Employment, Mr Michael Howard, it was clear that the strike this year was one of the main reasons why the Ford car company had decided to switch to Germany.

29 The Monopolies and Mergers Commission was called in after allegations that shop prices for instant coffee did not reflect the fall in world coffee prices.

30 The nearly worthless East German Ostmark was given parity with West Germany's strong Deutschmark.

31 Either because they want to be found indispensible or because they thought an uninterrupted fortnight with their family is more stressful than remaining at work.

32 The bank is designed to channel funds to East European countries to help them convert to market economies.

33 Because of late payments of some $100 million. The arrears to the four companies are part of a mounting number of defaults by the USSR caused, it is argued, by the growing pains of *perestroika*, as making decisions moves from central purchasing organizations to local enterprise.

34 The Transfer and Automated Registration of Uncertificated Stock; job losses are inevitable among the backroom staff in the City's security houses when the scheme, which entails the International Stock Exchange switching to a paperless settlement system, is fully operational.

35 International Automotive Design of Worthing, West Sussex. The company will make the new generation of LA 301 electric cars with Clean Air Transport of Sweden.

36 The issue of banknotes denominated in the European Currency Unit (ecu). The object is to take a practical step towards a common European currency while avoiding the inflationary dangers of the surrender of sovereignty involved in the French (Delors) plan.

37 Friends of the Earth and the Green Party accused British Nuclear Fuels of themselves being a polluter. Forty ultra-green organisations that might otherwise have participated withdrew because of the presence of BNF.

38 Restrictions would be imposed by Parliament on the present deluge of credit advertising and, in particular, the unsolicited mail offering gifts to people taking out loans.

39 Merton council, which was taken over by Labour in the May elections, intends to compete with the large numbers of entrepreneurs who sell goods during the Wimbledon fortnight of tennis championships.

40 Glenmorangie, which is number two in its sector in Great Britain and the market leader in Scotland.

41 Japanese extortionists, who arrive in force at annual shareholder meetings to disrupt proceedings by asking hundreds of awkward, mundane or irrelevant questions if the company does not pay them protection money to stay away.

42 Twenty-five billion German marks (£8.6 billion) in cash, ready for distribution from 1 July.

43 Rupert Murdoch of Sky Television. Satellite dish sales have topped 900,000 and should pass the one million mark by the autumn.

44 Warsaw, to administer its lending programme to Poland. It simultaneously announced a $250 million (£144 million) loan to help increase energy production and conservation.

45 The company agreed to buy up to 33 new Boeing 747-400 long-range jets in a deal worth more than £4 billion.

46 The sale, for £122 million, is part of the insurer's strategy to concentrate on its life and British general insurance concerns and reduce its exposure to risk.

47 The secrecy that surrounds some Swiss bank accounts. whereby clients are legally able to hide their identity behind lawyers and trustees.

48 Prudential Corporation; the move leaves it with about 500 offices compared with more than 800 in the late 1980s, its business having been badly hit by the housing slump.

49 One and two pence coins, a discovery that led the House of Commons public accounts committee to demand that they be replaced by cheaper copperplated coins, at a saving to the taxpayer of up to £4 million.

50 De Beers Centenary, the Swiss arm of South Africa's De Beers diamond group.

51 (26/7/90) What was ironic about the way in which the Soviet Union was able to pay all its outstanding debts to West German companies?

52 (3/8/90) Why were 4000 jobs axed from which British bank?

53 (11/8/90) The Department of Trade and Industry tried to enlist financial support for a £30 million amusement park, akin to a 'Disneyworld', to be built where? Construction is planned to begin in January 1991.

54 (14/8/90) Which company revealed that 93 of its 210 banks have refused to support its £2.5 billion refinancing proposals, leaving the company with a £610 million shortfall?

55 (15/8/90) Dramatic increases in interest rates and the slump in the housing market since 1988 led to what, according to figures published yesterday by the Council of Mortgage Lenders?

56 (15/8/90) Which mini-conglomerate company, trying to rehabilitate itself, announced that it is to concentrate on being a film and television company and sell the rest of its assets to reduce group debt?

57 (16/8/90) What is believed to be the largest bought deal on record in London to date?

58 (16/8/90) According to the latest figures from the Confederation of British Industry, manufacturing is now being worst hit by the economic slowdown in which area of the country?

59 (16/8/90) Which furniture and carpet group went into receivership, owing about £300 million?

60 (16/8/90) What is the purpose of Great Britain's first daily lottery, launched where and by whom?

61 (20/8/90) Fifty million British coins of which denomination, weighing together 675 tonnes, are gathering dust in bank vaults, at a cost of almost £4 million a year in lost interest, and why?

62 (21/8/90) A sharp fall in bank lending growth and the money supply in July provided evidence that high interest rates are curbing credit and spending. Lending by banks and building societies grew by only how much, the smallest monthly increase since when?

63 (22/8/90) What financial support for the unemployed was abolished in Australia by its Labor government?

64 (23/8/90) Which airline company, for what reason, is to close its London headquarters, move nearer to Gatwick and cut back on its 51 aircraft?

65 (25/8/90) According to a report in the business magazine *Management Today*, how many of the estimated 1.5 million Asian immigrants in Great Britain are now millionaires?

66 (31/8/90) A former City banking analyst and the chairman of Tomkins, the industrial group, joined forces to raise £100 million to form what bank and for what purpose?

67 (6/9/90) Whose photograph appeared on full-page newspaper advertisements for a relatively unknown anti-perspirant, called Mitchum, with the caption, 'For When You're Really Sweating'?

68 (6/9/90) Why was Sun Alliance, Great Britain's largest home insurer, swept into a £119 million loss in the first half of this year, down from an interim pre-tax profit of £191 million last time?

69 (7/9/90) August, the most crucial month in the motor distributors' year, when the new registration letter is introduced, saw what per cent fall in sales as against August 1989?

70 (13/9/90) How did Nelson Mandela, Swindon Town and Paul McCartney help Wembley, the leisure and property group?

71 (13/9/90) In what way did the Bank of England tighten the economic screw on Iraq?

72 (13/9/90) The Prudential, Great Britain's best known insurer, had no sooner announced £80 million losses incurred in the first half of the year through storms that it gave warning of further massive claims caused by what?

73 (13/9/90) Why did the Calor Group, the liquefied gas business, show a 20 per cent slide in interim pre-tax profits to £24.3 million?

74 (15/9/90) Which unit trust celebrated its 21st birthday in September?

75 (15/9/90) According to a report, what is the most economic way of providing for one's own funeral?

51 The announcement came less than two weeks after the West German Government agreed to provide a government guarantee for a DM5 billion bank loan to the Soviet Union. The funds to pay the debts will come from this loan. Thus, in effect, German banks will pay Russian debts to German companies, guaranteed by the German Government.

52 Midland Bank, after its chairman had apologised for 'clearly unacceptable' profits in the first half of the year. Before exceptional write-offs, the bank made profits of £74 million, down from £301 million. Shedding employees was an economy measure.

53 Despite the prospect of war in the area, the amusement park is to be built in Saudi Arabia.

54 Eurotunnel, the Anglo-French company. A threatened collapse of private funding has thrown the Channel tunnel project into doubt, at a time when there are only three miles to go before the tunnels from Great Britain and France meet.

55 More people had their homes repossessed in the first six months of this year than in any comparable period recorded—14,390 homes as against 7390 in the last six months of 1989 and 13,740 homes for 1989 as a whole.

56 Eagle Trust, which is being investigated by the Serious Fraud Office. However, the company's 32,000 shareholders were told not to expect any payment on their investment for at least three years unless some of Eagle Trust's complicated litigation bears fruit in the interim.

57 Imperial Chemical Industries sold its 24.9 per cent holding in Enterprise Oil for £680 million. A block of 113.26 million shares was sold yesterday to Warburg Securities and Cazenove & Co. at £6 a share.

58 The South-east, South-west and the West Midlands; a year ago, parts of northern England were most affected.

59 Lowndes Queensway, which trades from 270 stores, mostly out of London. Some 4000 jobs are at risk, but it is hoped that some of the stores may be sold as going concerns to other retailers.

60 Hospital Lotto, instigated yesterday by the five health authorities in Birmingham, may raise up to £1 million a year towards equipment for hospitals.

61 Fifty pence pieces, of which there is a superfluity. The excess was first noticed a year ago, when it was found by all banks that despite their distribution to customers, more were being

paid back in. The culprit, it is thought, is the £1 coin, first issued five years ago.

62 £3.9 billion, the smallest increase since August 1987, as personal and mortgage lending stagnated and retailers cut their overdrafts.

63 In a tough budget aimed at reducing welfare payments, the 380,000 people receiving indefinite unemployment benefits of $Aus 105 (£43) a week each would instead get $Aus 57 a week for up to a year.

64 Dan-Air, to save costs after the recent rises in fuel prices and a sharp decline in charter holiday bookings.

65 Up to 300; their total wealth is estimated at almost £2.6 billion.

66 The Bank of Edinburgh, which, it is intended, will buy small and medium-sized building societies in order to form a major mortgage and savings institution.

67 Arthur Scargill, president of the National Union of Mineworkers; at the time he was embroiled in financial uncertainties following questions arising from Soviet mineworkers' money donated during the miners' strike of 1984–5.

68 Sun Alliance suffered the most among the big insurers, following claims regarding the hurricanes that hit the country last year, because it stuck to a policy of only taking limited reinsurance in the Lloyd's market and meeting claims itself.

69 13.3%; August usually accounts for a fifth of business for the year. Sales this year dropped from more than 500,000 a year ago to 432,867.

70 Profits from the increased number of events at Wembley showed a 37 per cent increase before tax in the first half of the year.

71 By banning insurance payments to Kuwait and Iraq from midnight on 12 September.

72 Subsidence, related to the hot weather in the second half of the year.

73 The explanation appears to be because of the warmest winter since records began.

74 The Slater Walker High Income trust, now the MIM Britannia Income and Growth trust.

75 Those who wish to provide in advance for their own funeral do best to pre-pay for the event rather than save in a building society or insure against the inevitable.

1 (1/1/90) To keep the world's atomic clocks synchronized with the Earth's changing rotation speed, astronomers were obliged to make a time correction at midnight on 31 December 1989. What was it?

2 (2/1/90) What marred the festivities at the Brandenburg Gate of the first New Year jointly celebrated by East and West Berlin since the erection of the Berlin Wall?

3 (5/1/90) Which deposed dictator was the first foreign leader to be abducted and prosecuted in an American court?

4 (6/1/90) Which government ordered chastisement with a rattan cane, soaked overnight in brine, as a punishment for foreign workers who infringed its immigration laws?

5 (6/1/90) The French were outraged to learn in January that quantities of adulterated *foie gras* were freely circulating. Also in January, it was revealed that another counterfeit delicacy was on the market. What was it?

6 (8/1/90) On 7 January the Kremlin sent reinforcement troops to keep the peace between communities in which Soviet republic?

7 (9/1/90) Wooden posts on a Soviet border were set alight on 8 January. By whom and where?

8 (10/1/90) The Bulgarian Government established a commission to enquire into the death of Georgi Markov, a Bulgarian emigré killed in London some 12 years before. How was he murdered?

9 (11/1/90) Which Irish Roman Catholic priest was expelled from his missionary order of the Pallottine Fathers, and why?

10 (11/1/90) Why did two former Foreign Office ministers travel to Vietnam in January? Who were they?

11 (11/1/90) What major internal measure was implemented in China at midnight on 10 January?

12 (12/1/90) Estimates by NATO suggested that Soviet defence spending was more than that admitted by President Gorbachov. By how much and how were the figures misrepresented?

13 (13/1/90) In which east European country did the interim government outlaw the Communist Party?

14 (13/1/90) There were 99 public executions in Saudi Arabia in 1989, most for drug trafficking offences. What was the method of execution?

15 (15/1/90) Where did an electrical short circuit cause a fire that killed 43 people on 14 January?

16 (16/1/90) On 15 January, President Gorbachov signed a decree to send army, navy and KGB personnel to restore order in which area of the USSR?

17 (20/1/90) Which American mayor, of which city, was arrested for what?

18 (22/1/90) A three-week strike by municipal workers in which European capital city left it fouled with an estimated 80,000 tonnes of refuse on the streets by 21 January?

19 (23/1/90) A campaign was launched in the USSR to rename which of its cities?

20 Which head of government was the first to give birth while in office?

21 (29/1/90) On 28 January, the Chinese celebrated the start of their new year. In their calendar, each year is named in rotation after an animal. What is its name in 1990?

22 (31/1/90) In which city was the biggest McDonald's hamburger restaurant to date opened?

23 (2/2/90) What innovation was introduced regarding the crossword in *The New York Times*?

24 (3/2/90) Name three of the important measures announced by President de Klerk of South Africa in an historic speech on 2 February.

25 (5/2/90) An estimated 300,000 marched in the country's biggest street demonstration since 1917. Where did it take place? Where did the march culminate? What were the demonstrators demanding?

1 The duration of the year 1989 was extended by one second.

2 East German scaffolding collapsed on the Gate, killing two revellers and injuring 160 others.

3 General Manuel Noriega, recently dictator of Panama and accused of drug trafficking and other offences.

4 The government of Singapore.

5 A smuggling ring was importing low-grade white truffles from Italy and, after the application of walnut dye, offering them as the superior black variety from France.

6 Georgia, where tension was rising between the Georgian and Ossetian peoples.

7 By protesters from the Azerbaijan Peoples' Front, demanding an open border with their compatriots in Iran. The incident occurred near Ordubad in the Nakhichevan enclave, close to the Aras river.

8 Markov was jabbed with an umbrella tip containing a pellet with 0.2mg of the lethal poison ricin.

9 Patrick Ryan, wanted by Scotland Yard for terrorist charges, was expelled from the order for 'prolonged absences from the society and for persistent refusal to comply with the legitimate instructions of his superiors'.

10 Lord Ennals and Mr Timothy Raison went to monitor the treatment given to those refugees compulsorily returned from Hong Kong.

11 Martial law was lifted. It had been imposed in Peking seven months earlier following demonstrations in Tiananmen Square.

12 Twice the admitted £79 billion, because some military activities were given too low price tags.

13 Romania, the first such banning in eastern Europe. The decree was subsequently cancelled.

14 Beheading.

15 In a basement discotheque in Zaragoza, Spain. Most victims choked to death on smoke fanned by the air-conditioning system.

16 The Trans-Caucasus, where clashes between Azerbaijanis and Armenians were degenerating into civil war.

17 Marion Barry, the Mayor of Washington and one of the country's most prominent black leaders, was arrested for possession of the drug 'crack'.

18 Athens.

19 Leningrad, to rename it St Petersburg.

20 Miss Benazir Bhutto, Prime Minister of Pakistan.

21 The Year of the Horse.

22 Moscow.

23 By telephoning a certain number, a puzzler would be given the answers to any three clues.

24 The ban on the African National Congress would be lifted, political prisoners were to be freed, the death sentence was to be suspended and emergency restrictions on the media were to be abolished. Finally, it was announced that Nelson Mandela would shortly be released.

25 In Moscow—it was the biggest Soviet street demonstration since the 1917 revolution. The crowd marched through Moscow to the Kremlin, on the day before the Central Committee plenum. Condemning the slow pace of reform, the marchers demanded the removal of Kremlin conservatives and called for the end of Communist Party domination.

26 (6/2/90) In which country did experts claim that there was the worst outbreak of paediatric Aids?

27 (7/2/90) What object did a young Maori woman throw at the Queen when she was in New Zealand for celebrations to mark the 150th anniversary of the signing of the Treaty of Waitangi in 1840?

28 (8/2/90) In February, Soviet authorities ordered the publication of full details of what disaster that they had tried to keep secret for more than 50 years?

29 (8/2/90) In what momentous way was 70 years of Soviet history ended on 7 February?

30 (10/2/90) The world's leading meteorologists agreed, for the first time, that if economies continued as hitherto, global warming of 2°C–4°C would be inevitable after the year 2030. This would make the world hotter than at any time since when?: a) if the lesser warming took place? b) if the greater warming took place?

31 (15/2/90) 160 million bottles of what were suddenly removed from sale, and why?

32 (17/2/90) Which photographer won the World Press Photo prize and for what subject?

33 (20/2/90) Aleksandr Serebrov and Aleksandr Viktorenko returned to a greatly changed Soviet Union on 19 February. Where had they been?

34 (26/2/90) From 25 February, what became illegal on all domestic flights within the United States, save those lasting more than six hours to Alaska and Hawaii?

35 (28/2/90) In which country was a police inspector and the editor of a newspaper given government permission to fight a duel to the death, under a 1920 law allowing 'affairs of honour' to be thus settled?

36 (6/3/90) Into which 'independent' tribal homeland were South African police and troops sent, at the request of Brigadier Oupa Gqozo, who had deposed President Sebe in a bloodless coup, to restore order after rioting and looting by mobs?

37 (6/3/90) Islamic militants in Egypt, regarded as one of the most tolerant Arab countries, launched a campaign to outlaw which art form?

38 (7/3/90) Rabies got out of control in Poland during the Second World War, since when rabid animals have been found progressively farther west. Where was a rabid fox found, the nearest ever to the Channel?

39 (7/3/90) What was the main clause in the property bill which was passed by the Supreme Soviet?

40 (10/3/90) In what way was President Bush of the USA embarrassed by a telephone call, which he answered?

41 (12/3/90) Which president of what country went on hunger strike to highlight the economic plight of his people?

42 (12/3/90) For the first time, a hotel restaurant received the coveted third star in the *Guide Michelin*. Which restaurant was awarded the accolade?

43 (12/3/90) Which body was the first to take the decisive step of legal separation from the Soviet Union?

44 (13/3/90) What would happen, an official study predicted, if Japan's birth-rate continues at its present level?

45 (14/3/90) What did President Gorbachov describe as 'the most fateful decision in the history of the Soviet state'?

46 (14/3/90) In what way did Dermot Finucane and James Pius Clarke cause tension between the British and Irish governments?

47 (15/3/90) Which child therapist, one of the great figures of post-war psychology, committed suicide on 13 March at the age of 86?

48 (16/3/90) Who became the first Israeli prime minister since the Jewish state was founded in 1948 to lose a vote of no confidence in the Knesset? Which party is he leader of?

49 (16/3/90) In a survey of 422 Californian university students, 34 per cent of the men and 10 per cent of the women said that they had lied to get what?

50 (17/3/90) Why did Dr Jonathan Mann resign his post as director and founder of the World Health Organization's global programme on Aids?

26 Romania, where the former dictator, Ceauçescu, had designated all material related to the outbreak a 'state secret'.

27 A wet cloth, probably a T-shirt. The Queen remained unperturbed and the woman was apprehended by spectators and Maori warriors.

28 The Ukrainian famine of 1932–3, caused by Stalin's agricultural policies, in which it is thought over five million people died.

29 The Soviet Communist Party leadership agreed to end the party's exclusive right to rule.

30 a) 125,000 years if the lesser increase occurred. b) Three million years if the higher change took place. Such increases, caused by factors including carbon dioxide emitted from power stations and motor vehicles, would cause widespread changes in weather patterns, disruption of agriculture and a dramatic rise in sea levels.

31 Perrier mineral water. Traces of naturally-occurring benzene were discovered in bottles of the water on sale in the United Kingdom and other European countries. The use of benzene as a solvent has been linked with cancer. The loss to the company was estimated at £40 million.

32 Charles Cole of *Newsweek* magazine, for his dramatic shot of a sole protester facing a line of tanks in Beijing (Peking) during China's doomed democracy movement.

33 In space; the two Russian cosmonauts had left earth on 6 September 1989.

34 Smoking. Even on two-hour flights, some passengers had risked a fine of $2000 (£1175) by blocking smoke-detectors in aircraft lavatories with chewing gum and then illegally smoking tobacco.

35 Uruguay. The only permitted weapons are pistols. The last legal duel occurred in 1971, since when all requests have been rejected by the government. The challenge was issued to Federico Fassano, editor of the daily *La República*, who had published a story connecting the police officer to a smuggling case. Subsequently (6/3/90), the police inspector withdrew his challenge, saying his opponent 'is not worthy of the gentlemanly pursuit'.

36 Ciskei.

37 Belly-dancing.

38 Near Dieppe, less than 10 miles from the Channel. The disease has been spreading westward at the rate of about 25 miles a year.

39 Ownership of housing would henceforth be permitted. The bill was passed by 350 votes to three, with 11 abstentions.

40 He discussed the position of US hostages in Lebanon with—as he supposed—the President of Iran. The caller was in fact a hoaxer.

41 President Endara of Panama, whose economy is in ruins.

42 The Louis XV at Monte Carlo's Hôtel de Paris, whose chef is M. Alain Ducasse.

43 The newly self-named Supreme Council of the Sovereign Republic of Lithuania.

44 The population will be reduced to 45,000 in a millennium, and would then disappear.

45 The full Soviet voted by an overwhelming majority to institute the new post of Executive President and renounced the Communist Party's monopoly of power.

46 They were convicted terrorists who had escaped from the Maze prison in 1983 and had been recaptured. The Irish Supreme Court refused to extradite them to Ulster and ordered their release.

47 Dr Bruno Bettelheim, who had survived Nazi death camps. The Viennese-born psychologist had recently suffered a stroke and chose to die on the 13th, seemingly because it was the anniversary of the Nazi entry into Austria in 1938.

48 Yitzhak Shamir; the opposition mustered 60 votes, Shamir's Likud party and allies only 55.

49 Sexual partners. The figures are alarming because Americans for the past few years have been urged to question each other on their sexual antecedents to avoid 'high risk partners'.

50 He announced that he was leaving after disagreements on 'vital issues' with the director general of the organization, Dr Hiroshi Nakajima. It seems that their differences were mainly over whether Aids should remain one of WHO's highest priorities and on funding.

51 (17/3/90) Of the world's newspapers, which one was named newspaper of the year by *What The Papers Say*, television's longest-running current affairs programme in the United Kingdom?

52 (19/3/90) East Germans participated in their first free elections since the Nazi Party took power in 1933. The conservative Alliance for Germany won with 48.14 per cent of the 90 per cent of East Germans who voted. What per cent did the favourites, the Christian Democratic Union, gain? How many parties contested the election?

53 (19/3/90) The value of Nobel prizes will be increased this year by 30 per cent, making each worth what sum?

54 (21/3/90) Namibia became independent at midnight on 20 March and the new republic's flag was run up. What are its colours?

55 (22/3/90) What severe blow was delivered to Israel by Malev, Hungary's state-owned airline?

56 (27/3/90)How did Julio Gonzalez, a Cuban immigrant aged 36, make infamous United States history?

57 (28/3/90) Where, within the space of a week, were the remains of thousands of victims of Stalin's concentration camps found?

58 (29/3/90) In what way did the French Government declare war on the hazards of cigarettes and alcohol?

59 (30/3/90) By what majority of seats did Mr Bob Hawke's Labor Government in Australia retain power in the general election?

60 (30/3/90) The Belgian parliament voted to legalize abortion, leaving only which European Community country where it is still against the law?

61 (31/3/90) Why was a young American student at Oxford ordered to repay $50,687 (some £32,000) in tuition fees to the United States Navy?

62 (2/4/90) Of what fungicide did the US Government demand that French and Italian vintners certify that their wines for US import were free?

63 (2/4/90) The elections in Zimbabwe gave President Mugabe's ruling Zanu (PF) party a majority of 117 seats out of 120 in parliament. For what did Mugabe claim this gave him a mandate?

64 (2/4/90) Why did helicopters take to French skies to bombard agricultural and forest areas, in a £1.6 million campaign?

65 (5/4/90) Which monarch abdicated, for what reason and how was the ensuing constitutional crisis resolved?

66 (5/4/90) The remains, more than 50 million years old, of what new species of horse was found that may be the oldest ancestor yet known of today's horse?

67 (5/4/90) In which world area did Aids cases increase the most and, locally, by what per cent in 1989?

68 (6/4/90) East Germany's first freely elected parliament since the Nazi takeover in 1933 quickly dispatched the structures of 40 years of Communist rule. Whom did the parliament elect parliamentary president?

69 (7/4/90) The 20th anniversary of whose accession to power was marked by his inviting a *Times* journalist to accompany him on a *majlis*? What is a *majlis*?

70 (7/4/90) Which New York institution, founded by Jack Kriendler and Charlie Berns, began life as the 'Red Head', then became the 'Fronton', moved to 42 West 92nd St., and now can be found at 21 West 52nd St.?

71 (7/4/90) 23 veteran and vintage cars set off from London to Peking on a 13,200km rally. When was the first London–Peking rally?

72 (9/4/90) What was the name of the 10,513-tonne ferry vessel which, plying between Oslo and Frederikshaun in Denmark, caught fire, possibly as a result of arson.

73 (9/4/90) In what way did the teenager Ryan White, who died in Indianopolis aged 18, achieve world fame and the plaudits of public figures, including President Bush?

74 (11/4/90) What was the principal agreement between the French Government and Colonel Gadaffi of Libya that secured the release of three European hostages, held in captivity by the Libyan-backed Fatah Revolutionary Council in West Beirut?

75 (11/4/90) To what atrocity, committed under Stalin in 1940, did the Soviet Union finally admit?

51 *Argumenty I Fakty*, a Russian weekly with a circulation of 33.5 million copies.

52 41.9 per cent. The German Social Union gained 6.32 and the Democratic Awakening 0.91. 24 parties contested the election.

53 Four million Swedish crowns (£404,900).

54 Green, red and blue.

55 Malev bowed to threats by Islamic terrorists and announced that it was suspending flights of Soviet Jews from Budapest to Tel Aviv. Budapest had been a main transit point for Jews making their way from the USSR to Israel.

56 He was accused of being the worst mass murderer in the country's history by starting a fire that killed 87 people in a Bronx nightclub.

57 At Funfeiche, north of East Berlin, and then at Oranienburg nearby. Both are in the area used by the Soviet occupying troops when they administered the camps, hitherto controlled by the Nazis, from 1945 to 1948.

58 It announced that a law is to be introduced banning, from 1993, all direct and indirect advertising on television, in cinemas and newspapers, for cigarettes and tobacco, the consumption of which has been increasing. All alcohol advertising, for drinks containing more than 1 per cent alcohol, will also be banned on television and cinema screens.

59 The closest election in 30 years left the Labour Party victorious by eight seats. Mr Andrew Peacock immediately resigned as leader of the official Liberal Party, as it entered its fourth consecutive term out of office.

60 The Irish Republic.

61 He had recently discovered that he was homosexual and therefore barred from serving in the American forces. Some 24 liberal Congressmen, incensed at the injustice, sent a letter to the Pentagon protesting that the repayment order was 'punitive, unjust and unsupportable by legal authority'.

62 Procymidone, which is approved for use in Europe but, since it is not yet allowed in the United States, the Food and Drug Administration has not yet set any level in wine which can be tolerated.

63 A one-party state – although he was careful to concede that this might not be implemented immediately.

64 They dropped fish-scented rabies vaccine in an attempt to eliminate the disease in Europe's most dangerous carrier, the red fox.

65 King Baudouin I of the Belgians vacated the throne as a matter of conscience rather than sign a bill passed by parliament legalizing abortion, a ban on which had been in force for 100 years. Forty-two hours later, however, the Belgian Parliament voted unanimously that the King's 'inability to rule' had ended and he was reinstated.

66 The remains, named *Hyracotherium sandrae*, were discovered at Clark's Fork Basin in Wyoming, USA, and may provide researchers with valuable clues into a little known era of evolution. The horse's skeleton was no bigger than that of a present-day Siamese cat.

67 According to the World Health Organisation, southern Bolivia, Argentina and Uruguay reported an increase of 217 per cent, the largest increase in the western hemisphere.

68 Frau Sabine Bergmann-Pohl, a Christian Democrat and the first woman to hold the post.

69 Sultan Qaboos of Oman. A *majlis* is an annual journey whereby the Sultan and his cabinet leave their court to face citizens and petitioners in the countryside.

70 The '21' Club, originally a celebrated speakeasy.

71 1907.

72 The Scandinavian Star.

73 Ryan White was diagnosed as having Aids, contracted from a blood-clotting agent used to treat his haemophilia, when he was 13. He became internationally known the following year when he was barred from his school by officials who ignorantly thought he could spread the disease by casual contact. His mother won a legal battle to have him re-admitted, though his return was greeted by jeers and a boycott by some students.

74 The French Government, in contravention of a 1986 EC embargo, permitted the return to Libya of three Mirage jets, which had been impounded in 1986, having earlier been sent to France for overhaul.

75 The Katyn massacre of 15,000 Polish officers and men by the NKVD, forerunner of the KGB. The murdered men had been interned in the USSR in September 1939. Stalin tried to lay the blame on the Nazis, but documents recently made public leave no doubt as to the NKVD role.

76 (13/4/90) Which exiled European king was refused entry to his own country?

77 (14/4/90) Why did thousands of American children eschew tuna fish in school canteens and thereby proved themselves a powerful lobbying force against big commercial interests?

78 (14/4/90) Why did the Muslim fasting month of Ramadan, supposed to be the most spiritual on the Islamic calendar, produce the opposite effect in Egypt, where research indicated that Egyptians consumed more food in that month than in the other 11 of the year combined?

79 (19/4/90) Where and why did the misuse of pesticides by farmers cause large-scale human death and deformity?

80 (19/4/90) Which became the first constituent Soviet republic to produce its own currency?

81 (20/4/90) Where and in what country did a judge agree that a defendant had the right to ban all women from his jury?

82 (21/4/90) Where were thousands of people stranded, towns cut off and livestock killed over vast areas following the worst floods there in 30 years?

83 (23/4/90) How many veterans were among those who visited the 75th anniversary of the opening of which First World War battleground?

84 (23/4/90) In what way was the governance of Moscow reorganised by presidential decree?

85 (25/4/90) Many thousands assembled in Central Park, New York, to hear pop stars and politicians proclaim the new green gospel. What was the incongruous result?

86 (28/4/90) Hindu pilgrims splash in the holy water of the Ganges, despite its being polluted with potentially fatal consequences. Tens of thousands of bloated bodies, both human and animal, float by, many with vultures perched on them. What measures did the Uttar Pradesh government take to reduce the danger of disease?

87 (28/4/90) Hindu fundamentalists in the Indian Parliament won a battle to change the Hindi name for Bombay in all the official preceedings of the Lok Sabha (or lower house) to what?

88 (2/5/90) In what way were President Gorbachev, members of the Politburo, the Presidential Council and other city officials humiliated in Moscow during the annual May Day parade?

89 (3/5/90) Why were some 500 US and Canadian police moved into the St Regis–Akwesasne Mohawk Indian reservation?

90 (9/5/90) Which capital city, according to the Corporate Resources Group, has the highest cost of living?

91 (14/5/90) What make and model of second-hand car fetched a record £1,702,000 at an auction in Palm Beach, southern Florida?

92 (15/5/90) The world's population is increasing faster than ever before, with an estimated how many extra people likely to be born before the end of the century?

93 (18/5/90) Where was a royal burial, thought to be the richest unlooted tomb yet found, excavated in the New World?

94 (24/5/90) For what 'offence' was M. Jean-Marie Le Pen, the French extreme right-wing leader, ordered to pay a symbolic one franc (11p) fine?

95 (25/5/90) According to a report by the United Nations, the quality of life – measured by human longevity, knowledge and living standards – of which country came top?

96 (25/5/90) For what purpose did KQED, a San Francisco non-profit, educational television station, sue California's governor and the state prison authorities?

97 (29/5/90) Why did the descendants of Jacob De Haven sue the US Government for $141.6 billion ($83.8 billion).

98 (30/5/90) Boris Yeltsin was elected President of the Russian Federation by how many votes and what majority, causing President Gorbachev to express himself as 'somewhat worried' at the result?

99 (30/5/90) In future, bottles of wine for sale in the USA will carry on their labels what in addition to the usual vintage and name of vineyard information?

100 (2/6/90) What did a team from the Heological Survey of Western Australia find that British and other palaeontologists cautiously accept as the world's oldest fossilized plant?

76 King Michael of Romania. It was claimed by the Romanian Government that his planned visit, during which he intended to attend a rally, was political and not private.

77 They learnt that many thousands of dolphins die annually in nets used to catch tuna fish.

78 Egyptian newspapers reported stacked tables in most households for consumption in the hours between sunset and sunrise, when eating is permitted.

79 India, where illiterate farmers, unable to read the instructions, lavish massive quantities of pesticide on their crops.

80 Estonia, which signed a contract with an unnamed foreign firm to print banknotes with a face value of 100 million new krone to replace the Soviet rouble.

81 Queensland, Australia. A Mr Paul Shelly told a court in Brisbane that it was against his religion to be judged by women and the presiding judge accepted the plea, to the annoyance of legal, civil rights organisations and women's groups.

82 Areas of eastern Australia, which were engulfed by floods.

83 Five, all in their nineties, visited Gallipoli on the anniversary of the Allied landings.

84 There are now in effect two cities of Moscow: the capital of the USSR and, geographically the same area, another under the jurisdiction of the Moscow Soviet, or city council.

85 The audience left behind more than 150 tons of litter.

86 The introduction into the river of *Trionyx gangeticus* and *Lissemys punctata granosa*, meat-eating turtles that, though greatly reduced in number through hunting, have been for a long time resident along the 1500-mile Ganges.

87 Henceforth Bombay will be known as Mumbai instead of Bambai.

88 Some 40,000 demonstrators marched into Red Square for the second part of what was planned as a double May Day parade, the first being organised by official trade unions. Members of the second parade greeted Gorbachev and others of the official party on the Lenin mausoleum with whistles and shouts of 'shame', calling for the end of the economic blockade of Lithuania, the resignation of the Politburo en bloc, and for Mr Boris Yeltsin to be appointed president.

89 Two men had been killed in a day-long gun battle between heavily armed 'warriors' against 'traditionalists' who were opposed to a gambling business organised and run by the tribe. The reservation of six square miles straddles the borders between northern New York State, Ontario and Quebec.

90 Tehran, where the cost of living is almost twice that of London.

91 A 1907 Rolls-Royce Silver Ghost tourer, one of only four of its type still known.

92 Some one billion, roughly equivalent to the population of China. The present world population (5.3 billion) is increased every day by the birth of about 250,000 babies, or three a second.

93 Peru; the burial is nearly 2000 years old and is covered in gold and silver jewellery.

94 The fine was levied as damages by a civil court in the suburb of Nanterre for his having described the Nazi gas chambers as a 'detail' in the history of the Second World War.

95 Japan, followed by Sweden, Switzerland, the Netherlands, Canada, Norway, Australia, France and Denmark. Of the 130 nations surveyed, Great Britain came 10th, ahead of both the United States and West Germany.

96 To allow it to broadcast the final moments of Death Row inmates to television viewers.

97 Jacob De Haven, a rich Pennsylvanian merchant, who died penniless in 1812, lent George Washington's starving and beleaguered army $450,000, without which the army might not have survived intact and independence from Great Britain won. The sum claimed by his descendants was calculated at six per cent interest, compounded daily. That amount is now growing at $190 a second. It is estimated that the number of surviving relatives is at least 50,000 and may be as many as 500,000.

98 Yeltsin polled 535 votes to Aleksandr Vlasov's 467, four votes more than he needed in a third ballot.

99 A government health warning, cautioning customers that wine-drinking can impair driving skill, cause birth defects and, in addition, '. . . may cause health problems'.

100 A specimen similar to the brown seaweed *Hormosira*, which grew on earth 1.1 billion years ago. The seaweed fossils were found 90 miles north of the mining town of Newham, and if authenticated will predate by 600 million years the earliest known plant life ·

1 (21/2/90) Where did this potentially violent scene take place?

4 (12/4/90) Why is this waiter wearing a mask and where is he?

2 (27/2/90) Senior officers of which army are displaying what to photographers?

5 (23/6/90) Who is this man, and why is he doing what he is?

3 (11/4/90) What is incongruous about these two women?

6 (3/8/90) What building is this child and others surveying?

1 Amsterdam, where police raided a house occupied by squtters. Seven squatters and 51 of their supporters, protesting about property speculation, were arrested.

2 Officers of the Romanian Army hold up for examination by journalists electronic devices formerly used by Securitate switchboards to tap telephone conversations.

3 They are delegates to the World Ministerial Drugs Summit, held in London.

4 The waiter, pouring a drink for a customer in one of the lounges at Madrid airport, has protected himself against the smell of rotting refuse, accumulated through a week-long strike by cleaners. The customer seems manfully indifferent to the stench.

5 Bill Traverse, a Manitoba Indian chief, is waving a feather in opposition to the Meech Lake constitutional accord. By 23 June, Manitoba and Newfoundland were the only two of Canada's 10 provinces yet to sign; there were fears that the accord would grant Quebec too much political autonomy, although the package was effectively blocked on the ground that it discriminated against aboriginal people.

6 Our Lady of the Peace basilica in Yamassoukro, in the Ivory Coast. President Houphouet-Boigny's controversial basilica is thought to have cost over £86 million, an enormous sum for a small and impoverished state.

101 (2/6/90) Whose annual Pentecost pilgrimage to the top of Solutre rock in eastern France was featured in today's newspaper? What is the reason for the pilgrimage?

102 (9/6/90) Whom did the 300 members of the Russian Orthodox General Assembly elect to succeed the recently deceased Patriarch Pimen as the new Russian Orthodox Patriarch?

103 (14/6/90) Why did the British Government join a boycott of the sixth international annual conference on Aids in San Francisco?

104 (18/6/90) Which party in the Bulgarian elections came tenth, receiving 8338 votes – 0.14% of the total cast – when, according to the party spokesman, it should not have received any at all?

105 (18/6/90) What historical event was re-enacted on the same site, at a cost of £500,000 and after 6500 hours of preparation, by 2000 'actors' in a three-hour event that was watched by some 20,000 people?

106 (21/6/90) Why did President Bush of the USA suspend America's 18-month dialogue with the Palestine Liberation Organisation?

107 (21/6/90) Why was it estimated that Canadian Airlines will lose more than £20 million a year following an edict imposed by Ottawa?

108 (22/6/90) Where did an earthquake, which registered 7.3 on the Richter scale, kill more than 25,000 people, at first estimate, and injure tens of thousands more?

109 (22/6/90) What plot by right-wing conspirators was unmasked in the Republic of South Africa?

110 (23/6/90) What and why did the Soviet Union quietly start withdrawing from the secessionist Baltic republics, volatile southern republics and some Eastern European nations, according to US and NATO officials and independent experts?

111 (26/6/90) China made an important concession to the United States by allowing which Chinese dissident to leave the American embassy in Peking, where he had sought refuge, and remove himself to where?

112 (26/6/90) Why was a symbolic fine of one franc awarded against France's respected newspaper, *Le Monde*?

113 (27/6/90) What pledge, repeatedly given by George Bush and which helped him to the White House, was he forced to renounce and for what reason?

114 (27/6/90) What was believed to have been the biggest peacetime deportation in Italian history and why was it imposed?

115 (29/6/90) What declaration did the Foreign Office describe as the most far-reaching human rights document since the Helsinki declaration of 1975?

116 (2/7/90) On 1 July, China began a population census, a massive task in a country where, on average, how many children are born every day?

117 (2/7/90) Why did a congregation of Roman Catholics fight before the altar and down the aisle, exchanging punches and sending candles flying, after Sunday Mass at the St Maclou Cathedral in a northern suburb of Paris?

118 (3/7/90) Which celebrity, and why, went to St Patrick's Cathedral on Fifth Avenue, New York, fell on the knees at the door and shuffled forward on them along the 20-yard aisle to the altar?

119 (3/7/90) What caused the death of 1426 Muslims in a tunnel near Mecca, Saudi Arabia?

120 (4/7/90) What was the result of Chia Chia's visit to Mexico, for an indefinite stay beginning in late 1988?

121 (5/7/90) Who earned a reprise for 30,000 seals about to be clubbed and stabbed to death in South Africa to provide fur coats, dog meat and sex aids for the Far East market by offering to buy the seals for £13,000?

122 (5/7/90) The East German city of Rostock annulled the title of honorary citizen of which deceased German?

123 (6/7/90) To what was Manfred Werner, NATO's secretary-general, referring when he described a meeting as 'probably the most important summit in the history of our lives'?

124 (10/7/90) Which six countries in one of the world's most battle-torn regions pledged that to help find peace they would not interfere in each other's civil wars?

125 (11/7/90) In which country, seemingly in consequence of a public health campaign, did a majority for the first recorded time refrain from drinking wine?

101 President Mitterand, who vowed as a German prisoner-of-war that if freed he would tackle the stiff climb every year.

102 Aleksii of Leningrad, who defeated the 'traditionalist' candidate, Metropolitan Filaret of Kiev.

103 Because of the refusal by the United States to grant visitors' visas to anyone with HIV-I, the Aids virus.

104 The party for the Restoration of the Turnovo Constitution, the legal document which underpinned Bulgaria's constitutional monarchy before it was abolished in 1946. The party seeks the restoration of Tsar Simeon II.

105 The Battle of Waterloo, re-enacted to mark its 175th anniversary. Amateur soldiers came from Great Britain, Germany, France, Czechoslovakia, Lithuania, Italy, Russia; even a contingent of Canadian Redcoats were present.

106 Because neither Yassir Arafat, the PLO chairman, nor any spokesman had issued a condemnation of the failed terrorist attack on a crowded Israeli beach on 30 May.

107 Banning smoking on all flights.

108 Northwestern Iran, near the Caspian Sea. It was the worst earthquake in Iran since that of September 1978, which occurred in the same region and registered 7.7 on the Richter scale. Later the estimated number of dead was raised to more than 50,000.

109 A plan to assassinate President de Klerk and Nelson Mandela, the deputy leader of the African National Congress.

110 Nuclear weapons, because of fears that they might be stolen or seized as unrest grew in these regions. The weapons are being relocated in parts of the Russian republic close to central control and deemed to be relatively secure.

111 Professor Fang Lizhi and his wife Li Shuxian. The professor, who takes up a research post at Cambridge University, appears to have agreed to stop his sharp criticisms of the Chinese leadership, which had made him the country's best known dissident.

112 The case arose from an advertisement published by Le Monde almost six years ago, submitted by admirers of Marshal Pétain. Le Monde was found guilty of 'apologising for crimes and offences involving collaboration with the enemy', thereby breaching a law of 1951, drawn up specifically to prevent such material appearing in French publications.

113 His election pledge – 'Read my lips: no more taxes' – was rendered unsustainable in face of the spiralling budget deficit.

114 Italy deported 246 England football supporters after a street battle with police in Rimini during the World Cup games. Most of those deported protested their innocence.

115 The declaration agreed by delegates at the 35-nation human rights conference in Copenhagen.

116 50,000, or roughly 2083 an hour, or 35 a second.

117 An estimated 60 traditionalists tried to celebrate their own service in Latin. After a struggle of about an hour, during which a policeman tried unsuccessfully to mediate, the brawl ended when Father André Berrere agreed to say his Latin Mass in a side chapel.

118 Imelda Marcos, widow of the former Philippines president, who had just been acquitted on all charges that she plotted with her late husband to steal more than $200 million (£114 million) from her country.

119 The tunnel, at holy sites near Mecca, was designed to hold 1000 people; nearly 5000 pilgrims, however, were crammed in during this year's Haj (pilgrimage). Widespread panic erupted when a power failure stopped the ventilation system, cutting off air in the 500-metre tunnel. The temperature soared to more than 40 degrees, causing suffocation; others were crushed in the stampede to escape.

120 The giant panda, on loan from the London zoo, fathered a 4oz cub, the first born outside China to survive.

121 Mme Brigitte Bardot, the former actress. An open letter from her to President de Klerk led the South African government to suspend the cull 'in the light of misgivings about the procedure'.

122 Adolf Hitler.

123 The two-day Allied summit at Lancaster House, London, after which a joint statement was issued proclaiming that the Cold War was over and the Soviet Union no longer an enemy of the West.

124 Ethiopia, Uganda, Kenya, Sudan, Somalia and Djibouti, all countries of the Horn of Africa.

125 France, where alcohol abuse had reached alarming proportions; today 50.7 per cent abstain, women having been particularly responsive since 1980.

126 (12/7/90) After a close contest, who was elected deputy general secretary of the Soviet Communist Party?

127 (12/7/90) Which city in the USA did the Democrats choose as the site of their 1992 presidential convention?

128 (16/7/90) In which democracy did 13 government ministers resign during a week-end of political turmoil, the prime minister also doing so but then changing his mind?

129 (16/7/90) What Second World War French anniversary, falling on 16 July, went conveniently unremarked by government and people?

130 (17/7/90) What historic accord was reached between President Gorbachev of the USSR and the West German chancellor, Helmut Kohl, during the latter's second visit to the Soviet Union this year?

131 (17/7/90) Which Soviet republic, following the example of the Baltic republics, voted for sovereignty and planned to become a neutral state with its own army and currency?

132 (20/7/90) In what way did the 38th, 40th and 41st presidents of the United States honour the 37th and who are they?

133 (27/7/90) The private yacht of which prime minister was boarded and searched by a Royal Marine patrol and why?

134 (28/7/90) Which two countries, that have not yet signed a peace treaty ending the Second World War, seemed to be moving to an accord over what dispute?

135 (1/8/90) What criminal and inhumane act was perpetrated by French sheep farmers in the Vendée region and for what purpose?

136 (1/8/90) It was revealed that some 33,000 political prisoners in East Germany were delivered to West Germany in the last 25 years in exchange for what?

137 (1/8/90) According to a report published by the Senate judiciary committee in America, this year, at the present rate, will be the worst in American history for what and by how great an increase?

138 (4/8/90) Replicas of which three sailing ships were built in Huelva, Spain, for a two-year journey around Europe and America to mark what?

139 (6/8/90) Following the Iraqi invasion and occupation of Kuwait, a new government was imposed. What was it called and whom did Iraq appoint to the combined posts of prime minister, commander-in-chief of the armed forces, minister of defence and minister of the interior?

140 (7/8/90) In August 1990, the United Nations Security Council for the second time in its history imposed comprehensive economic sanctions. At which country were they directed, why and by what voting strength? Which countries abstained? Against whom were the first sanctions imposed, and when?

141 (9/8/90) What military activity was abolished for troops of the East German army on 8 August?

142 (9/8/90) How were two thieves, convicted of armed robbery in 1984, executed in western Sudan on 8 August?

143 (13/8/90) What was the code name given to international forces sent to Saudi Arabia against possible invasion by Iraq, after its seizure of Kuwait?

144 (13/8/90) Who was appointed to command of the British forces in Saudi Arabia and the Gulf, following Iraq's occupation of Kuwait?

145 (15/8/90) The leader of which country, having the day before met the Iraqi leader in Baghdad, flew to Washington to see President Bush and why?

146 (15/8/90) Voters in Montreal elected to parliament by a landslide Gilles Duceppe, aged 43, in Monday's federal by-election in Laurier-Ste Marie. He is believed to be the first MP elected principally on what platform?

147 (15/8/90) What decrees did President Gorbachev issue in respect of all those repressed by Stalin, save for certain narrow categories, and how will it affect them?

148 (16/8/90) Christian Brando, the son of Marlon Brando, the actor, charged with murdering his half-sister's boyfriend, was released on bail of how much in Los Angeles and what security was given?

149 (16/8/90) Marion Barry, the Mayor of Washington, convicted last week of possessing cocaine, announced that he will keep his pledge not to run for a fourth term this autumn. Instead he intends to seek what elected office?

150 (18/8/90) The town of Tarusa, south of Moscow, was featured on the front page of *Pravda* as being the first Soviet town since the Second World War to do what?

126 Vladimir Ivashko, the former president of the Ukraine and President Gorbachev's nominee, narrowly beat Yegor Ligachev, an outspoken Politburo conservative.

127 New York; unusually at this stage, however, the Democrats still lack heavyweight candidates to challenge President Bush.

128 India; the prime minister, Vishwanath Pratap Singh, who on Saturday said he had 'lost the people's trust', decided to stay after an emotional meeting with the leadership of his Janata Dal (People's Party).

129 Early on 16 July 1942, squads of uniformed French (Vichy) police, working from lists provided by French officials, first began arresting Jews in their homes around Paris. More than 13,000 Jews were detained within 48 hours, more than a third of whom were children born in France. Most were ultimately dispatched to Auschwitz.

130 President Gorbachev bowed to the inevitable and agreed to accept a united Germany in NATO, if that proved what the German people wished.

131 Ukraine, the second largest republic in the Soviet Union, which has rich industrial and farming resources.

132 Ex-presidents Gerald Ford (38th) and Ronald Reagan (40th) and the present incumbent, George Bush (41st), attended the opening ceremonies of Richard Nixon's (37th) presidential library at Yorba Linda, California.

133 The vessel, *Celtic Mist*, is the property of Charles Haughey, the Irish prime minister. He was not on board at the time. She was searched when in the waters of Carlingford Lough as part of routine operations·

134 Japan and the USSR; their dispute concerns the four southern Kurile islands, north of mainland Japan, which Tokyo claims were illegally occupied in 1945.

135 In a loathesome twist to the ceaseless struggle by French meat producers to protect their markets, a self-styled 'commando' of sheep farmers poisoned the feed of 200 sheep recently imported from Great Britain and held in the Vendée region for fattening, killing almost a hundred of them.

136 Oranges; troublesome suspects, if they did not know state secrets, were exchanged at DM95,847 (£32,300) a head via 'silent channels', in fact the evangelical churches in both Germanies.

137 Murders; if the present figures continue, there will be 23,220 murders in 1990, just over 63 a day, an increase of eight per cent on last year. The figures make the United States the most murderous of any industrialised nation, with a rate five times higher than Canada's and 13 times higher than in England and Wales.

138 The Niña, Santa Maria and Pinta, Christopher Columbus's ships which sailed to America. They are to make a journey to mark the 500th anniversary of the discovery of the New World.

139 The 'Provisional Free Government of Kuwait'; Colonel Ala Hussein Ali was appointed to the chief posts, but few Kuwaitis know who he really is.

140 Iraq, following its invasion of Kuwait. The decision was supported by 13 votes to nil, with Yemen and Cuba abstaining. The only previous decision by the UN Security Council to impose sanctions was in 1967, against Rhodesia.

141 Goose stepping, although soldiers were later photographed doing so while changing guard in East Berlin.

142 Suna, the Sudanese news agency, reported that Hamid Suliman and Arguci Turgawi Gareeb were crucified.

143 Operation Desert Shield.

144 Air Vice-Marshal Sandy Wilson, aged 49, a former fighter pilot.

145 King Husain of Jordan. It was seen in diplomatic circles as a desperate attempt by him to avert a military conflict between the United States, which had supported Jordan for many years, and President Saddam Hussein, his staunchest regional ally.

146 Duceppe, a union organiser representing the Bloc Québecois, campaigned on a platform that heavily relied on removing French-speaking Quebec province from the present Canadian federal union.

147 They were absolved and rehabilitated, which means not only that their good name is restored but can provide the basis for them and their descendants to reclaim residence rights in cities and to recoup position entitlements and other lost rights.

148 Two million dollars (£1.06 million), the actor putting up his Hollywood mansion as security.

149 A seat in the capital's city council.

150 Introduce bread rationing.

151 (20/8/90) Why was the body of an executed lieutenant-colonel in the Iraqi occupation forces in Kuwait hanged from a crane outside municipal headquarters?

152 (22/8/90) The parliament in Sofia voted to take what action when an anti-communist threatened to set himself on fire if it did not?

153 (23/8/90) President Bush yesterday authorised the call-up of an estimated 40,000 reservists as tension increased over Iraq's occupation of Kuwait. When was the last time an American president gave such an order?

154 (24/8/90) The RSPCA called yesterday for an end to the export of live animals after what barbaric outrage was perpetrated by French farmers at Thouars in the Deux-Sèvres department of France?

155 (24/8/90) What was presented to the Australian nation by Sir Geoffrey Howe, the deputy prime minister, because, he said, it was right that Australia should have its 'birth certificate'?

156 (27/8/90) According to a *Newsweek* poll, 43 per cent of Americans, nine per cent more than in a poll taken a fortnight ago, advocate what action to end the Gulf crisis?

157 (27/8/90) Why did Charles Haughey, the Irish prime minister, meet Brian Keenan at Dublin airport?

158 (27/8/90) Delhi and other northern Indian cities were in chaos for much of the week-end as high-caste students, apparently acting spontaneously and without leadership, went on the rampage in objection to what government plans?

159 (28/8/90) What is the purpose and capability of the American A10 Thunderbolt II, three squadrons of which were based in Saudi Arabia after Iraq's occupation of Kuwait?

160 (28/8/90) Who is Asif Ali Zardari and with what was he charged by police in Pakistan?

161 (28/8/90) What was carried by a special train, under KGB guard, from Bulgaria to Moscow?

162 (4/9/90) To whom did Geoffrey Palmer, the New Zealand prime minister, hand over power in the face of a leadership challenge?

163 (8/9/90) Voters in Ontario, Canada's largest province, rejected the Liberal Government and elected which party, despite its never having held federal power in Canada before?

164 (10/9/90) According to *Bild am Sonntag*, a popular West German newspaper, East Germany, to raise cash for its stricken economy, is ready to sell passports to Hong Kong Chinese for how much each?

165 (10/9/90) What item of clothing did some New York parents add to their children's school outfits and why?

166 (13/9/90) What was the title of the document, signed on behalf of the four Allied powers which defeated Germany in 1945, which will bring East and West Germany together as a single sovereign state?

167 (13/9/90) How many people, according to Amnesty International, were publicly executed in China between mid-January and the middle of August, making it the highest number in an equal period since when?

168 (13/9/90) Serbian opposition parties yesterday held a rally to demand what changes in electoral law?

169 (13/9/90) Why did a superior court jury in Los Angeles award $1.9 million (£1 million) to Bobby Coffey, aged 55, a dismissed Hughes Aircraft worker?

170 (13/9/90) Why did talks between British and Chinese defence experts break up in disagreement over the Hong Kong government's plans to move HMS *Tamar*?

171 (14/9/90) Why in Australia was a policy adopted of taking the pawprints of koalas?

172 (14/9/90) The Soviet Union plans to pass a law permitting what for wholly-owned foreign companies?

173 (14/9/90) What motor manufacturing company, for long defunct, opened a new factory today in Modena?

174 (15/9/90) Deprived smokers in the Soviet Union were given expensive relief during the tobacco shortage by what means?

175 (15/9/90) The programme approved by President Gorbachev yesterday for economic reform outlined the transition from central planning to a market economy, to be completed within what space of time?

151 To deter looters; around his neck was hung a placard reading, 'He stole the money of the people'.

152 Remove the red star and other Communist symbols from the building and the Bulgarian national flag.

153 The call-up was the first since North Vietnam's Tet offensive in 1968.

154 A lorry carrying 439 British sheep was set on fire by French farmers while it was parked outside an abattoir. The farmers claim that imports of cheap British lamb are reducing their income. Half the sheep were burnt to death; those that survived will probably have to be put down.

155 A copy of the document which ended Australia's status as a British colony in 1901 and created a nation. Great Britain this year amended her laws to allow a permanent handover of the original copy of the Australian Constitution Act, which Australia had had on loan since 1988. Great Britain's original reluctance to do so stemmed from the wish to preserve unbroken a series of archives that stretch back to the thirteenth century.

156 The assassination of President Saddam, but 80 per cent opposed a quick US attack on Iraqi positions. United States law forbids any involvement in assassination.

157 Keenan, after four and a half years held captive in darkened cells in Beirut, had been released by his Islamic militant captors and flown home by the Irish Government, whose intense diplomatic activity had secured his release.

158 To reserve more than a quarter of all civil service jobs for low-caste and tribal Indians, officially known as 'backward classes'.

159 Tank destroying aircraft, they are armed with the large 30mm GAU8/A Avenger cannon, which has seven rotating barrels capable of firing a continuous burst of 1174 shells from a single-drum magazine. Its shells, which weigh 1.6lb and travel at some two-thirds of a mile a second, can penetrate even the heaviest armour.

160 He is the husband of Benazir Bhutto, the ousted prime minister of Pakistan, and was charged with possessing illegal arms. Miss Bhutto said that the case against her husband was designed by the military to blackmail her and force her out of politics.

161 A consignment of 14 million cigarettes, to reduce the queues at Moscow's tobacco kiosks and prevent further demonstrations in which deprived smokers have blocked main roads in protest against the drug's scarcity. Cigarette rationing will be introduced in Moscow at the beginning of September.

162 Michael Moore, aged 41 and until today external relations and trade minister. After David Lange's surprise resignation a year ago, Palmer assumed office but was blamed for a disastrous fall in the party's ratings.

163 The New Democratic Party, which gained 74 of the provincial legislature's 130 seats. The Conservatives won 20 and the Liberals 36, a loss for them of 59 seats.

164 DM 1.5 million (£500,000).

165 Bullet-proof jackets, following a number killed and wounded this summer by stray bullets during street gun fights.

166 'On the final settlement with respect to Germany.'

167 Seven hundred, the largest since between 5000 and 10,000 people were shot in 1983.

168 About 20,000 people protested against the former Communist Party, now renamed socialists, and threatened to boycott elections.

169 The jury found that the company had retaliated against him for his uncovering alleged overcharges on government military contract work.

170 The government planned to move HMS *Tamar*, a British naval base, from the financial district to an island in the harbour, to make way for a harbour-front reclamation and development project.

171 In an effort to stop the animals being taken illegally from the wild to be kept as pets or in private parks. Researchers believe that, like humans, their prints are unique to each animal.

172 They will be permitted to operate on Soviet territory for the first time.

173 Bugatti, after an absence of nearly four decades.

174 Massive emergency supplies of Marlboro and other brands of cigarette were imported in a deal that will cost an estimated $1.9 billion (£1 billion) of hard currency.

175 Five hundred days.

1 (4/1/90) Why was the British weightlifting champion, Dean Willey, dropped from the Commonwealth Games in Auckland?

2 (6/1/90) In football, a former manager and a club chairman allegedly breached Football Association rules by placing a (winning) bet against their own club in an FA Cup tie at Newcastle United in January 1988? Which club is this?

3 (11/1/90) The British welterweight champion's hopes of a world title were shattered when he was surprisingly stopped in the seventh round by Buck Smith, a little-known American. Who is he?

4 (13/1/90) Professional skaters and coaches began a campaign to save which of Britain's great ice rinks?

5 (17/1/90) Which professional boxer, by knocking down Gerry Cooney in the second round at the Convention Center in Atlantic City, claimed the right to fight Tyson in the first $100 million contest?

6 (18/1/90) Which former world light welterweight champion was charged at Hackney police station in connection with the attempted murder of Frank Warren, a boxing manager?

7 (19/1/90) Who led the English cricketers on their unofficial tour of South Africa?

8 (22/1/90) Which former Wimbledon champion was banished from the Australian Open tennis championships, and for what?

9 (25/1/90) Which member of the Royal Family opened the 1990 Commonwealth Games in Auckland?

10 (26/1/90) Which British swimmers took the first three places in the 100 metres breaststroke final of the Commonwealth Games?

11 (29/1/90) Which tennis player won the Australian Open and in what way was his victory unusual?

12 (30/1/90) How much was promised by pools promoters to implement the Taylor report on the Hillsborough disaster?

13 (31/1/90) Which weightlifter at the Commonwealth Games was stripped of his gold medal and became the second to be disqualified after being tested positive for drugs?

14 (31/1/90) Who became the first woman swimmer to win five gold medals at a Commonwealth Games? How old was she?

15 (2/2/90) Which two-time winner of the men's singles at Wimbledon announced that he would be playing neither there nor in the French Open in 1990?

16 (3/2/90) Who became the first Scottish woman to win two Commonwealth Games medals by retaining her 10,000 metres title?

17 (5/2/90) Which British runner failed to appear for the 1500 metres heats in Auckland and for what reason?

18 (5/2/90) Where was it decided to hold the next Commonwealth Games, during the second fortnight in August 1994?

19 (6/2/90) How many gold, silver and bronze medals did the England Commonwealth Games team win?

20 (7/2/90) In what way was a new piece of miniature technology employed in Australia to photograph cricket matches?

21 (12/2/90) Which boxer was knocked out for the first time in his 38-bout professional career and why was the incident controversial?

22 (12/2/90) Which snooker player won the Benson and Hedges Masters title?

23 (22/2/90) Which football team went to the top of the first division for the first time in nine years after beating which opponent and by what score?

24 (26/2/90) By what score did Boris Becker beat Ivan Lendl in the final of the Stuttgart Classic?

25 (27/2/90) Why was the boxing bout between Lennox Lewis, the British-Canadian heavyweight, and Proud Kilimanjaro, cancelled shortly before the fight was scheduled at the Crystal Palace?

1 As a result of a positive drugs test.

2 Swindon Town.

3 Kirkland Laing.

4 The Richmond Ice Rink, which was threatened with redevelopment.

5 George Foreman.

6 Terry March.

7 Mike Gatting.

8 John McEnroe, three times Wimbledon champion, was fined £4000 and banished—the first instance of a player being disqualified in a grand slam tournament since 1963—for abusing the umpire, the grand slam supervisor and the tournament referee.

9 Prince Edward.

10 Adrian Moorhouse, James Parrack and Nick Gillingham, finishing in that order.

11 Ivan Lendl; his opponent, Stefan Edberg, had to retire in the third set with a stomach injury.

12 £50 million.

13 Ricky Chaplin.

14 Hayley Lewis, aged 15, of Australia.

15 Jimmy Connors, aged 37.

16 Liz McColgan.

17 Sebastian Coe, who was suffering from a viral infection.

18 Victoria, British Columbia, Canada.

19 47 gold, 40 silver and 42 bronze.

20 A camera, half the size of a cigarette, was embedded in the wood of the centre stump giving a new dimension, low down on the batsman's legs and his feet, to television coverage.

21 Mike Tyson, who was floored in the 10th round by James Douglas. Some, however, claimed that Douglas, who had been knocked down in the eighth round, was given too long a count. The fight was later declared void.

22 Stephen Hendry, who thus retained the title.

23 Aston Villa beat Tottenham Hotspur 2–0 at White Hart Lane.

24 6–2, 6–2.

25 Kilimanjaro refused to submit to the British Boxing Board of Control papers pertaining to a test for Aids which he had taken. This was thought to be the first time a boxer had refused to give the board the results of such a test.

26 (2/3/90) England won the first test match, their only victory against the West Indies since what year?

27 (6/3/90) Which British football club became the first to pass into Middle Eastern hands when a property developer, Sam Hashimi, bought a majority shareholding?

28 (12/3/90) Which driver won the United States Grand Prix, driving at an average of what speed?

29 (16/3/90) What record did Norton's Coin and his jockey, Graham McCourt, set by winning the Cheltenham Gold Cup?

30 (19/3/90) By what socre did Scotland defeat England in the rugby Calcutta Cup to win the Triple Crown and Grand Slam for only their third time?

31 (29/3/90) Why did Graham Gooch retire in the third Test match against the West Indies when it seemed that England was going to score a second victory, something no other team has achieved in 15 years?

32 (29/3/90) In which country was central funding of sport cancelled?

33 (2/4/90) By what time margin did Oxford win, as expected, the 136th University Boat Race and how many times did this give them victory in the last 15 years?

34 (4/4/90) Which commercial company, helped by Steve Cram, launched a £500,000 plus sponsorship for British athletics?

35 (7/4/90) How many horses were killed during the week's racing at Aintree, including the Grand National?

36 (9/4/90) Who became the second professional golfer to retain his US Masters golf title when he beat the US Ryder Cup captain, Ray Floyd, at the second hole of a play-off after they had tied, following four rounds with scores of 278, 10 under par?

37 (23/4/90) The 10th London Marathon was won for the first time by a Scot. What is his name, what was his time and how many runners competed?

38 (24/4/90) What distinction did Jahangir Khan, of Pakistan, uniquely achieve?

39 (30/4/90) Who became the Embassy World snooker champion, at what age and by beating whom?

40 (30/4/90) By what means was Anatoly Karpov, the Soviet Union's world chess champion from 1975 to 1985 and again the challenger for the title this year, defeated in a single game while simultaneously playing 24 opponents at a display in Munich?

41 (8/5/90) Sir Leonard Hutton's score of 364 against Australia had been unbeaten at the Oval since 1938. Which cricketer, on the same ground, eclipsed that by achieving an even higher individual score of how much?

42 (11/5/90) What identical feat was achieved by two members of the same family, one 37 years after the other?

43 (18/5/90) Manchester United, for the seventh time, won the FA Cup, this time in a replay at Wembley by one goal to nil against Crystal Palace. Which player scored the winning goal?

44 (21/5/90) Why did Roberto Baggio inadvertently cause 50 people to be injured, more than 50 arrested, and police in riot equipment and armoured personnel carriers to patrol the streets of Florence?

45 (23/5/90) The Whitbread Round The World Yacht Race was won by *Steinlager 2*, an 83-ft ketch with a 15-man crew. Which vessel finished second and by what time and distance margin?

46 (24/5/90) New Zealand had a four-wicket win over England in the first Texaco Trophy international. What record did the New Zealanders set by this?

47 (28/5/90) What world record was broken by Mr Roy Anderson, a professional stuntman, in Toronto?

48 (31/5/90) What silver sporting trophy, stolen in 1970, was found near a rubbish tip close to Bingley, West Yorkshire?

49 (4/6/90) Why did a spokesman for the Coastguard, based at Lee on Solent, describe the Round the Island Yacht Race, a 52-mile circumnavigation of the Isle of Wight, as 'totally chaotic'?

50 (7/6/90) By what margins were the winning horse and the second and third separated on reaching the finishing post of this year's Derby?

26 1974.

27 Sheffield United.

28 Ayrton Senna driving a McLaren at an average speed of 90.5 mph.

29 The odds—100/1—made Norton's Coin the longest-priced winner of the Tote Cheltenham Gold Cup.

30 13–7.

31 A blow on his left hand broke a bone and he was sent to hospital for treatment.

32 Czechoslovakia. The central funding body for sport under the Communists was abolished and with it went the guarantee of state support.

33 Oxford finished in 17 min 15 sec, Cambridge in 17 min 22 sec. This was Oxford's 14th win in the last 15 years.

34 Lucozade, which in a three-year deal will become the official drink supplier at main meetings, beginning with the United Kingdom championships at Cardiff on 2 and 3 June.

35 Six.

36 Nick Faldo of Great Britain. The only other player to have won the title in successive years (1965 and 1966) was Jack Nicklaus.

37 Allister Hutton, aged 35; he finished in 2 hours, 10 minutes and 10 seconds, ahead of a field of 25,450, the greatest number of entrants to date.

38 He became the first man to win nine successive British Open squash titles.

39 Stephen Hendry, a Scot, beat Jimmy White 18–12, to become the youngest-ever winner of the title at 21 years and four months. The winner's cheque was for £120,000.

40 He lost the game to the Mephisto-Portorose Chess Computer, manufactured in Germany. Never before had a computer beaten a player who was held the world championship. Karpov commentated: 'It was the same as against Kasparov (the world champion). I made one mistake and then it was over.'

41 The Lancashire left-hander Neil Fairbrother, who made 366 against Surrey. Lancashire also notched up a record, for their total score of 863 beat their highest of 801 against Somerset in 1895 and improved on the best in a county championship at the Oval.

42 Peter Hillary, the son of Sir Edmund Hillary, accompanied by two fellow New Zealanders, reached the summit of the 29,028-ft peak of Mount Everest. Sir Edmund made

mountaineering history when, on 29 May 1953, he became, with his Nepalese guide, Tenzing Norgay, the first man to attain the summit.

43 Lee Martin in the 60th minute. The left back, a local man, had cost Manchester United nothing.

44 On 17 May Florentina 'sold' Baggio, the international mid-field player, to Juventus for the record sum of 24 billion lire (£12 million). Two nights and two days of rioting and street fighting ensued, quelled only when police used batons and tear gas against crowds throwing stones and bottles. Two hundred extra police had to be called in to reinforce the local garrison.

45 After 128 days' sailing and 32,932 nautical miles from the Needles to the Horn and back, the ketch *Fisher and Paykel*, also from New Zealand, finished in second place only two miles and 30 minutes behind the winner. *Steinlager 2* is the only vessel in the event's history to win the race outright as well as all six individual legs.

46 The tourists' 298 for six wickets was the highest score by a side batting second in a one-day international event.

47 He jumped 21ft 3in from one five storey warehouse to another, eclipsing the previous record of 19ft, despite pulling a hamstring.

48 The Rugby League World Cup. It stands 2ft 6in and was last seen when on display at the Midland Hotel, Bradford, in 1970. The cup is decorated with players in action but has no markings to indicate its purpose or depict previous winners.

49 The Coastguard was called to a record 27 incidents – in one of which a competitor died. The race had an entry of 1541 yachts, with some 7000 crew in total. The first incident involved the yacht *Xeryus*, which hit the wreck of a Greek cargo ship off the Needles and capsized. There were 15 incidents involving vessels, most between the Needles and St Catherine's Point; 51 people were rescued, of whom 12 were admitted to hospital. A further 33 people required assistance by the rescue services. The cause of the disasters is not as yet known, since the weather was unexceptional, save for a strong westerly force five wind blowing against the direction of the tide, causing rough seas.

50 *Quest For Fame* finished three lengths ahead of *Blue Stag*, with *Elmaamul* 1½ lengths away, third.

51 (8/6/90) Ten days after reaching first division football for the first time in its history, which club, and why, was demoted to the third division?

52 (11/6/90) At the age of 30 years and three months, Andrés Goméz of Ecuador won his first grand slam title in the French Open at Roland Garros by beating whom and by what score?

53 (18/6/90) The Wimbledon lawn tennis championships received an official seal of approval after the completion of a £2 million improvement programme by the All England Club. Apart from the safety certificate, what effect will the improvements have?

54 (18/6/90) What myth about his talent did Ivan Lendl dispel in the final of the Stella Artois tennis tournament at Queen's Club?

55 (25/6/90) What was the name and type of vessel which broke the cross-Atlantic speed record and why was there resistance to her being awarded the title of the Blue Riband?

56 (27/6/90) Name the substitute football player who, by scoring a single goal against Belgium, qualified England for the quarter-finals of the World Cup.

57 (27/6/90) Which former Wimbledon champion was defeated in this year's first round of the men's singles and by whom?

58 (28/6/90) Who was the last of the British entries to be eliminated during the men's singles championship at Wimbledon. In which round was he defeated, by whom and by what score?

59 (4/7/90) Which sport, deemed to violate civil rights, was banned in New York State?

60 (6/7/90) Which four women, and which four men, reached the semi-finals of the Wimbledon singles championships?

61 (8/7/90) Which competitor created Wimbledon history by becoming the first to win nine single championships?

62 (9/7/90) For the first time since which year, the Wimbledon men's singles went to five sets. Who were playing, who won and by what score?

63 (9/7/90) West Germany defeated Argentina in the World Cup 1–0 with a disputed penalty, but the event was marred by disgraceful Argentinian conduct in which, among other incidents, the Mexican referee was assaulted. What occurred for the first time in a final as a result?

64 (11/7/90) In the last decade, which produced record-breaking high jumps, distance running and many other athletics, what sport showed no real improvement in players' performance?

65 (12/7/90) The Forestry Commission banned which group of sportsmen from its woodlands?

66 (13/7/90) Which British gambling activities raked in a record £1881 billion in the year to March, £161 million more than in the previous year?

67 (16/7/90) What announcement was made by which British sportsman at the end of yesterday's Foster's British Grand Prix at Silverstone?

68 (21/7/90) Which British javelin thrower set what world record?

69 (21/7/90) In what way did Pierre-Andre Gobet, a Swiss marathon runner aged 35, break a world record?

70 (27/7/90) On the first day of the Cornhill Series at Lord's, what was achieved that has not been seen in England for five years, and by whom?

71 (28/7/90) Graham Gooch scored 333 in the first Test against India at Lord's. This was how many runs less than the record, scored by whom, and made Gooch one of how many players to score a Test triple century?

72 (28/7/90) On the same day (27 July), what other record was set by whom at Swansea during the match between Warwickshire and Glamorgan?

73 (31/7/90) Graham Gooch, the England cricket captain, scored 333 in the first innings against India at Lord's; in what way did he become unique on the fourth day's play? And in what way did Kapil Dev, the Indian all-rounder, establish a Test record on the same day?

74 (9/8/90) Which football club, faced with a winding-up order that threatened to lose the club its Football League status, was saved by a man aged 19, and how?

75 (15/8/90) Which batsman, and at what age, became the second-youngest Test century-maker and was largely responsible for saving the Old Trafford Test for India?

51 Swindon Town; the demotion, imposed by the Football League, was in response to Swindon's making illegal payments to players.

52 He defeated Andre Agassi, an American, in four sets, winning by 6–3, 2–6, 6–4, 6–4.

53 A cut of 30,000 in spectator capacity, creating an unprecedented demand for tickets.

54 By defeating Boris Becker 6–3, 6–2 to become champion, he demolished the generally held belief that he was never at his best when playing on grass.

55 The *Hoverspeed Great Britain*, a massive catamaran, made the crossing in three days, seven hours and 54 minutes, cutting 2½ hours off the previous record. Officials, however, were divided on whether the contest was open to hovercrafts.

56 David Platt. London bookmakers promptly made England third favourites at 9–2, behind Italy and West Germany.

57 John McEnroe, three times Wimbledon winner and number four seed, was defeated in three straight sets (5–7, 4–6, 4–6) by Derrick Rostagno.

58 Jeremy Bates, the last of seven home players, went out in the second round when beaten 6–1, 3–6, 6–4, 6–1 by Derrick Rostagno. It was the first time that no British player has reached the third round of the men's singles at Wimbledon.

59 Dwarf throwing. The practice was introduced to America from Australia three years ago. Competitors, usually in bars, swing a dwarf twice before hurling him onto a pile of mats. Dwarfs wear helmets and padding with handles. The record of 16 feet was set in Florida last year.

60 Ladies: S. Graf (WG), L. Garrison (US), M. Navratilova (US) and G. Sabatini (Arg). Men: I. Lendl (Cz), S. Edberg (Swe), G. Ivavisevic (Yug) and B. Becker (WG).

61 Martina Navratilova (US) by defeating Zina Garrison (US) 6–4, 6–1.

62 S. Edberg (Swe) beat B. Becker (WG) 6–2, 6–2, 3–6, 3–6, 6–4. Edberg served two aces, Becker five.

63 Two Argentine players were sent off; never before had the red card been shown in a final.

64 Dr Alastair Cochran, of Aston University, a leading physicist, told the first World Scientific Congress of Golf in St Andrews that the sport had advanced by a mere two per cent. The average drive hit on the American professional circuit had increased by only six yards, and the median score in the British Open had improved by only 3.3 strokes since 1984.

65 Wargames enthusiasts; the commission believe that they damage trees and disturb wildlife.

66 Great Britain's casinos, according to Gaming Board figures.

67 Nigel Mansell, Great Britain's most successful racing driver since James Hunt, the former world champion, announced that he would retire from Grand Prix racing at the end of the year.

68 Steve Backley, aged 21, set the record by throwing a javelin 90.98 metres, making him the first to exceed a throw of more than 90 metres.

69 He became the fastest conqueror of Mont Blanc, jogging up and down Europe's highest peak (15,466ft) in five hours, 10 minutes, beating by 19 minutes the previous record set in July 1989.

70 Two players—Graham Gooch and Allan Lamb—both scored Test match centuries in the same innings. At the end of the first day, Gooch had made 194 not out, Lamb 104 not out.

71 Gooch's 333 was the sixth highest Test match score, 32 runs short of Sir Garfield Sobers's record. There has not been a higher individual score at Lord's. Gooch became the 11th man to score a Test triple century.

72 Tom Moody, a Western Australian who plays for Warwickshire, scored cricket's fastest century when he reached 100 in only 26 minutes off 36 balls.

73 Gooch hit 123, bringing his total to 456 runs, a world aggregate for a single player in a Test match. He also became the first player in Test history to score a triple century and a single century in the same match. Dev, for his part, hit four successive sixes off Eddie Hemmings, the off-spinner, to establish a Test record for sixes in a Test match over.

74 Aldershot, a fourth division club, was saved from extinction by Spencer Trethewy, who invested £200,000 of his own money to sustain it. The young entrepreneur made his fortune in property.

75 Sachin Tendulkar, aged 17 years and 112 days, scored 119 not out in the second innings. Only Mushtaq Mohammad, of Pakistan, has scored a Test century at an earlier age, when 17 years and 82 days, against India in 1961.

76 (16/8/90) Which tennis player beat Ivan Lendl, the world number two seed, in the ATP championships and by what score?

77 (17/8/90) The NatWest Trophy semi-final between Lancashire and Middlesex at Old Trafford was again rained off yesterday, raising the possibility of the cricketing equivalent of a penalty 'shoot-out' to settle the issue. When is this brought into play and of what does it consist?

78 (17/8/90) Tom McClean, arriving in Falmouth, Cornwall, became the first man to achieve what by doing so?

79 (17/8/90) What chess record was set yesterday by George Hassapis in his match against the American Orest Popovych?

80 (21/8/90) Research at Southampton University seemed to suggest what method of making money when betting on race horses?

81 (22/8/90) Which county, the first this season to inflict defeat on Middlesex, leaders in the county cricket championship, were penalised 25 points and why?

82 (23/8/90) What is the nature of the fourth annual olympics held in the hamlet of Crooked River Ranch in Oregon, USA?

83 (25/8/90) On the second day of the third Cornhill Test, India in the match against England amassed 606 runs for nine declared. What record did this establish?

84 (27/8/90) Ayrton Senna celebrated the signing of his new contract with the Honda Marlboro-McLaren team by winning which race in immaculate form?

85 (28/8/90) What cricket record was broken by whom on Sir Donald Bradman's 82nd birthday?

86 (29/8/90) Stefan Edberg, the top seed, was beaten in the first round of the United States Open at Flushing Meadow by whom and by what score?

87 (31/8/80) What British athlete, having fallen in the 1500 metres final at the European athletics championship, was reinstated in an unprecedented move in track and field, and why?

88 (16/8/90) Which spokesman of the Green Party was dropped as presenter of BBC's programme *Sport on Friday* and why?

89 (16/8/90) For what reason did police arrest 22 people in dawn raids on homes throughout the country, part of an exercise named Operation Boarhunt?

90 (6/9/90) Four years ago, Birmingham bid to stage the 1992 Olympic Games; in the event, Barcelona secured the nomination. Which city made a bid to bring the 1996 Olympics to Great Britain?

91 (10/9/90) Which player beat whom in a surprise finish to the Women's Singles final at the US Open?

92 (11/9/90) Where is the £28 million Don Valley athletics Stadium, planned to open on 16 September?

93 (11/9/90) Who became the first German rider to win the Du Maurier international in the 15-year history of the Spruce Meadows show?

94 (11/9/90) To whom was the French America's Cup yacht *F1* sold and what was unique about the sale?

95 (13/9/90) Tottenham Hotspur yesterday confirmed that secret talks had been held with whom regarding a cash injection?

96 (13/9/90) Which football team scored a surprise victory over Austria in Sweden in the European championship?

97 (13/9/90) By what score did West Germany retain the Three Nations hockey cup by defeating whom in Rotterdam?

98 (15/9/90) Next month the International Rugby Football Board meets in Edinburgh to decide what?

99 (15/9/90) Two Rugby football clubs, Richmond and Blackheath, proposed a scheme involving a voluntary code of conduct to eliminate what?

100 (15/9/90) What was the name of the British two-tonner that won the last race of the Sardinia Cup?

76 Malavai Washington, an unknown American, unseeded and ranked number 103, surprised the tennis world by winning in straight sets, 6–2, 6–3.

77 Had weather prevented the two teams completing at least a 20-over match, the result would have been settled by five bowlers from each team bowling two balls each at an unguarded set of stumps. The team with the most hits would advance to play Northamptonshire in the Lord's final on 1 September. In the event, play was resumed, leading to Lancashire's victory.

78 He became the first man to cross the Atlantic in a 'bottle', a voyage he hopes will raise £500,000 for the National Children's Home. The 11-tonne, bottle-shaped *Typhoo Atlantic Challenger* took 37 days to cover the 2950 miles from New York.

79 George, a north London boy aged six, became the youngest player ever to beat a master. He took 10 minutes and 19 moves

80 The best way to beat the bookies, it transpired, is to place bets at the last moment and at the bookmakers' board price, not at the starting price. Analysis of some 100,000 betting slips over two years revealed that punters who took the board price came out 47 per cent ahead, while those who settled for the starting price lost half their money. Those placing bets in the morning, prior to pre-race information being available in the shops, achieved average results, losing about a quarter of their stakes.

81 Derbyshire; after the match a five-man panel from the Test and County Cricket Board unanimously agreed that the pitch at Derby was 'clearly unfit for first-class cricket .

82 The annual Short and Fat Guys' Road Race attracts entrants from all over the USA and Canada. Competitors 'run' the one-mile downhill course. The rules, described as 'very liberal', are unusual: competitors must pull into the compulsory halfway pit-stop, where beer and hot buttered sweetcorn are served, and all the 'runners' cross the finishing line at the same time.

83 This was India's highest score against England in 78 Test matches.

84 The Belgian Grand Prix; he led from start to finish in the 44-lap race.

85 Australia came to England in 1930 and played five tests. Bradman, in seven innings, scored 974 runs, an average of 139.14. He scored one triple century, two doubles and one

of 131. Graham Gooch, the England cricket captain, yesterday beat this record, which has stood for 60 years, when he scored his 1058th Test run this season.

86 Alexander Volkov, who comes from Kaliningrad, a town on the Baltic Sea, won 6–3, 7–6, 6–2 in just under two hours. This was the first time the top seed had lost in the first round since Jan Kodes beat John Newcombe in 1971.

87 Peter Elliott, the pre-race favourite, was awarded a place in the race after being pushed down with 600 metres to go by Hauke Fuhlbrugge of East Germany. Elliott was awarded Fuhlbrugge's place.

88 David Icke was replaced, the BBC saying that though he had given 'excellent service' it was time for a 'fresh face'.

89 The 22 were suspected of being involved in the violent disorders at the Bournemouth–Leeds United game at the end of the football season earlier this year.

90 Manchester; its bid was rejected on 18 September, when the 88 members of the International Olympic Committee cast their votes in Tokyo. The next Olympics will be held in Atlanta, Georgia.

91 Gabriela Sabatini beat Steffi Graf in straight sets.

92 Sheffield, it is built on the site of a former steel works.

93 Otto Becker, on *Optiebeurs Pamina*.

94 The yacht was sold to a United States syndicate: it is the first time in the 158-year history of the trophy for a challenger and defender to collaborate.

95 Robert Maxwell, the publisher; talks concerned the possibility of his taking a minimum 25.1 stake in return for investment. The talks had ceased, it was stated, but may reopen.

96 The Faroe Islands won 1–0, Torkil Nielsen scoring the decisive goal in the 63rd minute.

97 West Germany defeated The Netherlands 3–0.

98 Whether the amateur regulations that govern the sport should be relaxed, a recent poll indicating that a majority of the public believe players should be allowed to earn money from playing the game.

99 The 'poaching' of players from other clubs.

100 *Juno*; Italy came second, West Germany third.

1 (31/1/90) What unusual task have these professional firemen undertaken?

4 (21/6/90) What order and nationality of monks are these and why are they seemingly disorderly?

2 (14/5/90) Lively conversation at the Glaziers' Hall, London. What was the object of the meeting?

5 (25/6/90) An unusual view of the Champs Elysées in Paris. Why, and in what way, was the famous avenue temporarily transformed?

3 (19/6/90) Where was this giant model of a radio placed and why?

6 (24/7/90) To what purpose are these women parading, and where?

1 They are filling a 5000-gallon pool erected on the stage of the Globe Theatre, London, for Alan Ayckbourn's latest play, *Man of the Moment*. The pool weighs 38 tons when full.

2 The two, scrutinised by a judge (centre), were among 26 people trying to talk their way to the Conversationalist of the Year title. The event, sponsored by *Whitaker's Almanack*, raised funds for Spina Bifida and Hydrocephalus.

3 To mark the 50th anniversary of General de Gaulle's wartime call to arms from London, the model, relaying his speech, was erected in the Place de la Concorde, Paris. It was made from scaffolding and plastic sheeting.

4 Franciscan monks at San Mauro monastery, Sardinia, who had received dispensation to stay up late, are cheering Italy's goals against the Czechs in the football World Cup.

5 Wheat, grown on pallets and brought in overnight by 800 farm labourers on 460 lorries, was a publicity stunt to improve city-dwellers' image of European farmers. The 'crop' is being examined by a French policeman.

6 The centre figure is the winner of a beauty queen contest in a Soviet women's penal colony at Chelyabinsk in the Urals; the others are runners-up. The contestants made their dresses from pieces of material from the prison.

1 (30/12/89) What was the Royal Ballet's pantomine production for January 1990?

2 (30/12/89) '. . . a dazzling state-of-the-art lighting display and a virtually limitless supply of worshippers to throng the nation's arenas, this promises to be the most extravagant Grand Guignol laid on yet by one of rock's most illustrious performers'. Of whose concerts, beginning on 3 January, was this said? And what 'special feature' prefaced each concert?

3 (30/12/89) Malcolm Nabarro conducted, among other pieces, *The Wasps* Overture, *Dream Children* and *The Three Elizabeths* at The Maltings, Snape on 1 January 1990. Name the composers of these three works.

4 (30/12/89) The English National Opera went into the New Year with two outstanding productions. What were they?

5 (3/1/90) Which leading American singer/songwriter and notable born-again Christian played six nights at the Hammersmith Odeon?

6 (13/1/90) On 3, 4, 5 Feb at the Royal Albert Hall, two American blues guitarists joined Eric Clapton in concert. Who were they?

7 (13/1/90) On 8 Feb, again at the Royal Albert Hall, Eric Clapton presented a concerto for guitar. Who wrote the score, and on what scores had performer and composer previously collaborated?

8 (16/1/90) A gifted young cellist, Alexander Baillie, was loaned for life by an anonymous sponsor a cello valued at £200,000. By whom was the cello made?

9 (17/1/90) Which choreographer and dancer threatened to withdraw all his works for the coming season from the Ballet of the Paris Opera, and why?

10 (17/1/90) Who deputized in January for Placido Domingo, then suffering from influenza, and received acclaim for taking at short notice the title role in Verdi's *Otello* at Covent Garden?

11 (18/1/90) Which American musician was pictured offering financial aid to Václav Havel's new Czech government?

12 (20/1/90) A boxed set of soundtracks to Peter Greenaway's films, including *The Draughtsman's Contract* and *Drowning by Numbers*, was reviewed. Who composed them?

13 (3/2/90) Which Borodin opera was revived at Covent Garden this month?

14 (3/2/90) Re-releases of two 1940 concerts by a seminal blues singer/writer under the title *Alabama Bound*, and of two French sessions (1969 and 1977) by a veteran Kansas band leader, singer and pianist, entitled *Roll 'em* were enthusiastically reviewed. Name the artists.

15 (12/2/90) Which Russian musician returned to the Soviet Union to perform, 16 years after he had been stripped of his citizenship?

16 (17/2/90) Following the success of a documentary about this musician by Bruce Weber, the release of the albums *Let's Get Lost* and *The Route* (the latter a collaboration with Art Pepper) celebrated whose work?

17 (17/2/90) A memorial concert for which outstanding pianist was held at the Barbican? And with which pianist did he share the first prize at Moscow Tchaikovsky Piano Competition in 1962?

18 (24/2/90) 'From 1964 until 1970, her voice was the perfect instrument for a remarkable run of hit songs composed by Burt Bacharach and lyricist Hal David'. Who is being described?

19 (24/2/90) What favourite opera of Agatha Christie's was featured in a new production by the Welsh National Opera, sponsored by Agatha Christie Limited?

20 (3/3/90) A major new musical began previews at the National Theatre today. What is it, who is it by, and from what does it take its theme and setting?

21 (3/3/90) Whose London concerts, accompanied by the Count Basie Orchestra, were part of the launch celebrations for Jazz FM?

22 (21/3/90) Westminster City Council authorized a £175 million redevelopment scheme for the Royal Opera House in Covent Garden. How will this affect the Floral Hall?

23 (31/3/90) Which new touring band were consistently referred to (in *The Times*) as the 'Antiques Roadshow'?

24 (31/3/90) 'Hyperactive 13-piece French troupe with a raffish brand of electro-rai fusion' Who was thus described?

25 (31/3/90) Music from a 1961 session by two Jazz maestros, *Together for the First Time* and *The Great Reunion*, has been re-released and was reviewed today. Who were they?

1 Ashton's *Cinderella*.

2 Paul McCartney. An 11-minute film produced by former Beatles collaborator Richard Lester.

3 *The Wasps* is by Vaughan Williams, *The Dream Children* by Edward Elgar and *The Three Elizabeths* by Eric Coates.

4 David Pountney's 1950s-style production of *Hansel and Gretel* and Prokofiev's *The Love For Three Oranges*.

5 Bob Dylan.

6 Robert Cray and Buddy Guy.

7 Michael Kamen. Clapton and Kamen had previously scored the television series *Edge of Darkness* and the film *Lethal Weapon 2*.

8 Joseph Guarnerius.

9 Rudolf Nureyev, principal choreographer was outraged that the contract offered to him contained the unprecedented clause that he should have no say in casting.

10 Jeffrey Lawton, who had started singing professionally only when he was made redundant as a mail order salesman.

11 Frank Zappa.

12 Michael Nyman.

13 *Prince Igor*.

14 Leadbelly and Jay McShann.

15 Mstislav Rostropovich, the cellist and conductor.

16 Chet Baker.

17 John Ogdon, who shared the 1962 Moscow Tchaikovsky Piano Competition prize with Vladimir Askenazy, who appeared at the memorial concert.

18 Dionne Warwick.

19 Richard Strauss's *Der Rosenkavalier*.

20 *Sunday in the Park with George*, by Stephen Sondheim and James Lapine, inspired by Georges Seurat's painting *La Grand Jatte*.

21 Ella Fitzgerald.

22 The Victorian building will be incorporated into the Opera House as a foyer but local residents fear that it will entail the destruction of most of it.

23 The Notting Hillbillies.

24 Les Negresses Vertes.

25 Louis Armstrong and Duke Ellington who, surprisingly, had not recorded together before 1961.

26 (7/4/90) Georgie Fame, the British jazz keyboard player, appeared with which prolific Irish performer at Wembley Arena?

27 (13/4/90) Whom did Kurt Masur replace as musical director of the New York Philharmonic Orchestra?

28 (23/4/90) What gamble did La Scala opera house take in staging Verdi's *La Traviata*?

29 (27/4/90) What was revealed about Mozart in a letter discovered in a private house from him to his father, penned by his wife?

30 (9/5/90) Which opera company, one of England's oldest, moved from London, why and to where?

31 (12/5/90) Which 69-year-old musician featured in The Times A–Z Guide to Rock today?

32 (12/5/90) Which outstanding pianist was described thus, following his concert at the Barbican: 'Dressed in black, the maestro appears from a small back door, forbids the presence of biography or programme notes, and is more than reluctant to take applause.'

33 (12/5/90) Which House music performer, who made his sudden rise to fame (in only 14 months) by playing acid house parties and 'raves', topped the charts with *Killer* this month?

34 (18/5/90) WOMAD weekend was held at Morecambe. What do the initials stand for?

35 (18/5/90) £528,000 was paid at Sotheby's in London for a heavily revised manuscript, thought to be the only autograph source of which of Beethoven's works?

36 (19/5/90) Born before the invention of the phonograph, he played the cello at the premier of Verdi's *Otello*, and conducted an outstanding recording of Verdi's *Requiem* in 1951. All his recordings are now released on compact disc and video. Who was he?

37 (26/5/90) A new production of a Benjamin Britten opera, directed by Sir Peter Hall, was presented at Glyndebourne. What was it, and who was the eponymous star?

38 (27/5/90) What happened at Spike Island in the Mersey today?

39 (20/6/90) Which opera singer, one of the world's greatest sopranos, announced her retirement and for what reason?

40 (20/6/90) Which two of Great Britain's leading colleges of music were advised to combine as a London conservatoire or face second-rate status?

41 (23/6/90) Classic recordings by which jazz saxophonist (who died in April) have begun to be systematically re-released?

42 (24/6/90) The Royal Opera gave a special performance at Kenwood, in the open air, of which work, in support of Weizmann Aid, Cancer research?

43 (25/6/90) The Ampex reel-to-reel tape recorder, used by which singer to compose music, was sold at Sotheby's in New York for $14,300 (£8,937) to an anonymous bidder?

44 (5/7/90) Which rock group made its first stage appearance on English soil since 1982 and where?

45 (7/7/90) Who has Jane Hermann replaced as artistic director of the New York-based American Ballet Theatre?

46 (7/7/90) Which male Columbian-born dancer performed in *Pillar of Fire*, *La Bayadère* and *Gaité Parisienne* at the London Coliseum?

47 (7/7/90) Where is the setting for *The Intelligence Park*, Gerald Barry's opera, receiving its long-awaited première at the Almeida?

48 (10/7/90) What musical instrument, stolen from whom in 1987, is being held for ransom of £1.5 million by a gang thought to be connected to the Calibrian 'N drangheta, hitherto infamous mainly for the ruthlessness of its human kidnappings?

49 (14/7/90) An expected 72,000 people were denied admission to Wembley Stadium, because of what minor injury to whom?

50 (14/7/90) Who currently holds the 'officially recognised' record for the largest audience ever assembled for a single performer?

26 Van Morrison.

27 Zubin Mehta, who had held the post for the last 13 years.

28 For 26 years La Scala had shunned productions of *La Traviata* because it was too closely associated with Maria Callas and productions there after her last performance in the role had been greeted with catcalls, scuffles and even stink bombs thrown at the stage. The new production, however, was raptuously received and Tiziana Fabbricini, in the Callas role, acclaimed a star.

29 That Mozart, at the age of 27, eight years before his death in 1791, was suffering from a life-threatening illness. The letter, which Mozart was too ill to write himself, provided proof that his wife, Constanze, was devoted to him, and not as she had been portrayed in some biographies of the musician.

30 The D'Oyly Carte Opera, main standard bearer of the Gilbert and Sullivan tradition, moved, because of financial problems, to Birmingham's Alexandra Theatre with effect from January 1991.

31 John Lee Hooker.

32 Michelangeli.

33 Adamski.

34 World of Music, Art and Dance.

35 His *Sonata for Cello and Piano* in A major (opus 69), one of his greatest works for two instruments. Beethoven wrote the sonata in 1807/8.

36 Arturo Toscanini.

37 *Albert Herring* with John Graham-Hall

38 The Stone Roses, darlings of the British independent music revolution, staged a sell-out concert.

39 Dame Joan Sutherland, after a career of nearly 40 years, so that she may 'be remembered by her past performances'. The Australian-born opera singer will make her last performance in September and October, when she stars in Meyerbeer's opera *Les Huguenots* at the Sydney Opera House.

40 The Royal Academy of Music (founded in 1822) and the Royal College of Music (1881). A report by the Polytechnics and Colleges Funding Council stated that continued independence could not provide sufficient high quality professional musicians to maintain the necessary standard of excellence in the country's symphony orchestras and its soloists.

41 Dexter Gordon.

42 Puccini's *La Bohème*.

43 It had been the property of the late Buddy Holly and was sold, together with other effects, including sweaters, glasses and guitars, by his widow. The items were virtually sold out, realising $703,615 (£439,759), twice Sotheby's estimate.

44 The Rolling Stones, at Wembley Stadium, before an estimated audience of about 70,000.

45 Mikhail Baryshnikov.

46 Ricardo Bustamante, of the American Ballet Theatre.

47 Dublin.

48 A priceless Stradivarius violin, made in 1717, the property of the French musician Pierre Amoyal. The instrument was stolen when Amoyal stopped his car outside a tobacconist near Turin to buy cigarettes, the car being driven off by the thief within seconds.

49 A performance by the Rolling Stones was cancelled because Keith Richards, the lead guitarist, had sustained a quarter-inch cut on a left hand finger which turned septic, preventing his playing and causing a postponement of the concert.

50 Tina Turner, whose concert at the Maracana Stadium in Rio attracted 180,000.

51 (14/7/90) Whose life and works have been celebrated at the small palace at Hohemems in Austria annually for the last 15 years?

52 (14/7/90) Haydn's *E flat major sonata*, Chopin's *Fantasie – Impromptu, Op 66*, *Nocturne, Op 55 no 2* and *A flat major Etude, Op 25 no 1*, and Liszt's *Weinger, klagenk, sorgen, zagen* all feature on whose *Last Recordings*?

53 (20/7/90) Whose appearances in Hyde Park in the morning attracted more attention than at Wembley Stadium in the evening?

54 (21/7/90) What musical extravaganza took place in the shadow of the Brandenburg Gate today?

55 (23/8/90) For what item of whose clothing did the Hard Rock Café of Los Angeles pay £16,500?

56 (24/8/90) What is the name of Prince's fourth movie sound track?

57 (25/8/90) A judge in Reno, Nevada, ruled that which British band was not responsible for the suicide of two youths and why had the case been brought?

58 (25/8/90) Whose Twelfth Symphony was premiered at the Three Choirs Festival, an event which was hailed as the 'renaissance of a gifted composer who has suffered long and cruel neglect for the sin of Tonality'?

59 (25/8/90) What unusual musical assemblage featuring the works (in this order) by Bach, Tchaikovsky, Dukas, Stravinsky, Beethoven, Ponchielli and Mussorgsky will be revived this December?

60 (29/8/90) Which three tenors shared the number two spot in the Gallup-Music Week charts, usually occupied by rock and roll performers?

61 (1/9/90) Which orchestra, performing in London this month, has over the last 30 years enjoyed musical direction by George Szell, Pierre Boulez, Lorin Maazel and, currently, Christoph von Dohnànyi?

62 (1/9/90) Which leading New York avant-garde band, currently on tour in Great Britain, are edging uncomfortably close to commercial success, despite the fact that their latest album *Goo* conformed to the tradition 'of looking and sounding as unpleasantly cheap and radical as possible'?

63 (1/9/90) Who was the unlikely subject of the first programme of a new season of Thames Television's The South Bank Show?

64 (1/9/90) Who featured in what work, mounted in the Cleveland San José Ballet at Edinburgh this weekend?

65 (1/9/90) The leading Texan blues guitarist, Stevie Ray Vaughan, was killed in a helicopter accident on 27 August. What was the name of his regular touring band, and to which David Bowie album did he make a notable contribution?

66 (1/9/90) Which 23-year old rock group had difficulty selling tickets for their concert at Wembley Stadium today?

67 (8/9/90) DJ Jazzie B is the producer, writer and arranger of which pop and fashion phenomenon?

68 (8/9/90) 'Imagine a huge orchestra trying simultaneously to evoke every sound in New York.' What piece of music, performed by the Junge Deutsche Philharmonie under the direction of Pierre Boulez at the Festival Hall, was thus described?

69 (8/9/90) The English National Opera opened its 20th century season with which work—described by producer David Pountney as 'the greatest opera written in our century'?

70 (8/9/90) Who, amidst blanket media coverage, asked us to *Listen Without Prejudice*?

71 (8/9/90) Which conductor, who was to have led the Last Night at the Proms on Saturday, was replaced. Why, and by whom?

72 (15/9/9/) Who were described, at the beginning of a major UK and world tour, as having 'an aural effect akin to the sensation of having a car battery dropped on the foot'?

73 (16/9/90) A recording of a gala performance by which three singers was broadcast on Channel 4 this evening? What occasion did the concert originally mark?

74 (18/9/90) Which long-standing African dance company appear at Sadler's Wells Theatre tonight?

75 (21/9/90) Which American musician, at 66 still playing 250 concerts a year, was the subject of a BBC1 *Omnibus* profile tonight?

51 Schubert. In 1991, the festival will be held at nearby Feldkirch, but it is hoped it will revert to Hohenemes the following year.

52 Vladimir Horowitz.

53 Madonna, whose morning jogs with her 'minders' provoked regular antagonism with press and admirers alike. Her three concerts at Wembley received mixed critical reaction.

54 A performance of *The Wall*, organised by ex-Pink Floyd singer and songwriter, Roger Waters.

55 A black leather outfit worn by the pop singer Michael Jackson, which was featured on the cover of his album *Bad*.

56 *Graffiti Bridge*. The album covers four sides but gives little indication of what the forthcoming film is about.

57 The heavy metal band Judas Priest; it had been claimed by the dead youths' families that the album, *Stained Class*, contained a subliminal message on the disc, which the youths had been listening to before their suicide.

58 George Lloyd.

59 Walt Disney's *Fantasia*, in a newly restored print.

60 Luciano Pavarotti, with the World Cup theme song version of Verdi's *Nessun Dorma* from *Turandot*, and the Spaniards José Carreras and Placido Domingo. The recording of the concert which they gave together in Rome on the eve of the World Cup final was deprived of top place among the albums only by the fact that its release coincided with that of Prince's *Graffiti Bridge*.

61 The Cleveland Orchestra.

62 Sonic Youth.

63 George Michael.

64 Rudolf Nureyev in *Coppelia*.

65 Double Trouble; Vaughan played lead guitar on Bowie's *Let's Dance* (1984).

66 Fleetwood Mac. At the beginning of the week, ticket agents were offering tickets at less than half-price in an attempt to boost attendance. Also on the bill were venerable 'progressive rock' warhorses Jethro Tull and Hall and Oates.

67 Soul II Soul – essentially a brand-name for a style of music popular in clubs and its associated styles of dancing and dress.

68 *Amèriques* by Edgard Varèse.

69 *Wozzeck* by Alban Berg.

70 George Michael, whose latest LP bears this title.

71 Mark Elder, after stating that he would consider removing stirring nationalist anthems, such as *Land of Hope and Glory* and *Rule Britannia!* if war broke out in the Gulf, was replaced as conductor for the climax of the Proms season by Andrew Davis, chief conductor of the BBC Symphony Orchestra, who proved himself more mindful of the occasion and of the audience's wishes.

72 Heavy-metal group Iron Maiden.

73 José Carreras, Placido Domingo and Luciano Pavarotti, who were recorded at the Baths of Caracalla in Rome on the eve of the World Cup Final. This 'repeat' included material not shown when the concert was first transmitted.

74 Les Ballets Africans, from Guinea.

75 Blues guitarist B. B. King.

1 (30/12/89) 'I'm a great believer in making a party work . . . We initiate new people with questions on what certain things mean to them, which animals they like most—and which animals they think they are most like.'

2 (3/1/90) 'After a decade of achievement, let us herald the decade of hope.'

3 (4/1/90) 'The pay levels of teachers are too low, administrative burdens too great, the pace of change too hectic and unsettling.'

4 (6/1/90) 'I really put my foot in it this time. I should not have left the nunciature.'

5 (25/1/90) Which playwright said of the theatre: 'This is an art which only very rarely can sustain itself on box office alone.'

6 (31/1/90) 'Most of us women like men, you know. It's just that we find them a constant disappointment.'

7 (2/2/90) 'Oh, so you're the one who won all the medals.'

8 (5/2/90) 'We read the dictionary. It's always by our bed. On his side is an English one, a Collins, and on my side an American, Random House.'

9 (12/2/90) 'Our struggle has reached a decisive moment. Our march to freedom is irreversible. Now is the time to intensify the struggle on all fronts. To relax now would be a mistake which future generations would not forgive.'

10 (14/2/90) 'The embryo is the start of life and must be given the same status as a child or a grown-up person—or as a member of the House of Lords.'

11 (17/2/90) 'When one talks about painting it's all nonsense. It has its own language and anything else is a bad translation.'

12 (17/2/90) 'When people see me swimming they know that I am physically fit, and when they hear of me playing bridge they know I am mentally fit'.

13 (20/2/90) 'I think they are pernicious but they do exist and we have to deal with them in a commonsense way.'

14 (21/2/90)'I've not had too many problems with men, its women. We have a long way to go in this country before women can accept other women for the way they look and the money they earn.'

15 (22/2/90) 'Many workers are seeking counselling from our medical staff and if some of them are especially worried, the proper advice may be for them not to have a family.' Who said this and why?

16 (28/2/90) She . . . 'had her rebellious moment, but it was pretty quiet compared to mine, which lasted about 15 years.' Who, of whom?

17 (3/3/90) 'I don't need any help. I only need directions to the nearest pub.' Who said this and what had just happened? What had he been attempting to do?

18 (7/3/90) 'I think women have been around in politics long enough for them to be dealt with—to coin a phrase—as "one of us".'

19 (10/3/90) 'Thank God I wasn't all that good as a drummer; if I had been I'd probably still be playing the things.'

20 (14/3/90) He is 'a prattling political pygmy'. Who, of whom?

21 (16/3/90) 'Mrs Thatcher wanted him alive. We send him back in a box.'

22 (17/3/90) 'Do you dance to it or send messages?' Who said this, and what was the object in question?

23 (21/3/90) 'I do wish I had brought my chequebook. I do not believe in credit cards.'

24 (28/3/90) 'Very neat hair is a sign of anxiety, rather like having a box of paper hankies in the back window of a car.'

25 (31/3/90) 'I wasn't the first poet to be arrested, and I'm not the last. I'm just lucky.'

26 (31/3/90) They speak of 'employment, love of life, fear of death, pleasure, passion, sensuality, voluptuousness, sex, drink.' Who of what?.

27 (3/4/90) 'I call it post-pop. It's after Andy.' Who, of what?

28 (4/4/90) 'When you are lying drunk at the airport, you're Irish. When you win an Oscar, you're British.'

29 (6/4/90) '. . . something has gone quite badly wrong.'

30 (7/4/90) 'I suppose we judged our social scale to some extent on whether the wife went out to work.'

1 Jeffrey Archer, former Deputy Chairman of the Conservative Party.

2 Margaret Thatcher.

3 Cardinal Basil Hume, Archbishop of Westminster.

4 General Manuel Noriega, deposed dictator of Panama, to his American captors on his flight to Miami to face drug trafficking and other capital charges.

5 Arthur Miller, the American playwright, in London for the opening of his play, *The Price*.

6 Clare Short MP.

7 According to Haley Lewis, a swimmer, the Queen said it to her in Auckland when she was presented. Lewis was the first woman to win five gold medals at the Commonwealth Games.

8 Marianne Wiggins, wife of Salman Rushdie, the novelist.

9 Nelson Mandela, in a speech after his release from more than a quarter of a century in jail.

10 The Duke of Norfolk.

11 Francis Bacon, quoted in a review of his retrospective exhibition at the Tate Gallery, Liverpool.

12 Deng Xiaoping.

13 Judge Pickles, of drugs, during a radio interview in which he called for possession of cannabis to be legalized.

14 Selina Scott.

15 Dr Roger Berry, director of health and safety at Sellafield, the Cumbrian nuclear plant, after it was disclosed that there was a likelihood of a child's developing cancer if its father had been exposed to radiation at the plant before the child was conceived.

16 Mick Jagger of his daughter, Jade.

17 Mr Brian Edwards to rescuers after he crash landed his Tiger Moth biplane in the Kent countryside after it lost its propeller. He had hoped to fly to Australia in it.

18 Sir Geoffrey Howe.

19 Paul Raymond.

20 Norman Tebbit of Neil Kinnock.

21 Latif Nassif Jassem, the Iraqi Information Minister, to Arab reporters after the hanging of Farzad Bazoft, an *Observer* journalist accused of spying, whose body was returned to the British Embassy.

22 The Prince of Wales, in Nigeria for the first official visit by royalty in 30 years, to Colonel Raji Rasaki, Governor of Lagos, who had just presented him with an exceedingly large 'talking drum'. The Prince was informed that it was for sending messages.

23 Mrs Margaret Thatcher, at the Ideal Home Exhibition, which she visited shortly before the budget.

24 Joanna Lumley.

25 Exiled Soviet poet Irina Ratushinskaya.

26 John Hoyland of his abstract paintings and prints.

27 Mr Paul Warhola, older brother of the late Andy Warhol, discussing an exhibition of his oil paintings (including a Heinz Beans can homage to his brother).

28 Brenda Fricker, surprise winner of the Best Supporting Actress Oscar for her performance in *My Left Foot*.

29 Mr Robin Leigh-Pemberton, Governor of the Bank of England, commenting on the rise in inflation.

30 Norman Willis, General Secretary of the TUC.

31 (11/4/90) 'If you sat a little monkey at a typewriter for 100 years you couldn't invent her.'

32 (12/5/90) 'I'm not against snogging, but I'd rather do it in a car. What I hated was 22 other girls standing around the light bulb while you were being kissed. That wasn't my idea of growing up.'

33 (12/5/90) 'The trouble is that the barber in Peru won't get it.' Who, to whom of what?

34 (14/4/90) 'There is nothing more traditionally British than our distaste for discussing sex.'

35 (19/5/90) 'My grandfather was a rat catcher on the Sandringham estate. But my mother would always call him "a vermin exterminator".'

36 (26/5/90) 'A fox once dashed across in front of my pram. I still remember where it happened.'

37 (29/5/90) 'If we had no intention of handing over power, we would not have had these elections.'

38 (7/6/90) 'I do not regard myself as a horse.'

39 (15/6/90) 'Never in my wildest dreams a year ago would I have ever told you that this kind of openness . . . would be unfolding.'

40 (19/6/90) There would not be 'some great wodge of tax or something dropping out of the sky'.

41 (22/6/90) 'I refuse to shoot from the hip.'

42 (25/6/90) 'Even if they come here and claim it, we are not going to give it to them.'

43 (28/6/90) 'What a load of pap.'

44 (4/7/90) 'It was fate. Had they not died there, they would have died elsewhere and at the same predestined moment.'

45 (12/7/90) 'I think the odds are that it's over.'

46 (14/7/90) 'It's the first show I've ever missed in 27 years. It's like I've blotted my copy book.'

47 (25/7/90) '. . . what I am in favour of is the harnessing of the best aspects of ancient and modern medicine to contribute towards the most effective healing of the patient's mind and body.'

48 (26/7/90) 'I walk my dog, listen to music, relax with my wife.'

49 (14/8/90) 'Dr Carey is a great champion of the Bible and with the amount of whizzing about he will have to do I imagine this would be just the job.'

50 (14/8/90) 'No point in getting into all these semantics. The main thing is to stop the oil from coming out of there.'

51 (15/8/90) 'Breast-feeding cannot be kept to the family home or clinic.'

52 (16/8/90) 'I only have to sit in my car and a thousand come to kiss my hand.'

53 (17/8/90) '. . . thousands of Americans . . . will go home in shrouded coffins.'

54 (17/8/90) 'Look him [Leon Brittan] up. I think you'll find he's a German Jew, telling us what to do with our English laws.'

55 (21/8/90) 'Hundreds of thousands of children [in the UK] have educational experiences not worthy of a civilised nation.'

56 (21/8/90) 'I am always getting into hot water, even boiling water, but this should be only lukewarm.'

57 (22/8/90) 'Talk about Margaret Thatcher and you talk about somebody who stands tall when the going gets tough. You talk about somebody who knows what it is to have a moral compass.'

58 (28/8/90) 'Bollocks.'

59 (29/8/90) 'When greed is in the saddle, respect of the law is cast aside.'

60 (31/8/90) 'Hostage is crucifying aloneness. There's a silent, screaming slide into the bowels of ultimate despair. Hostage is a man hanging by his fingernails . . .'

31 Peter York of designer Vivienne Westwood.

32 Pamela, Lady Harlech.

33 Groucho Marx to S. J. Perelman of a proposed scene which parodied *The Merry Widow* in the latter's script of *Monkey Business*, in a feature on *Calman at the Movies*.

34 James Tye, director general of the British Safety Council, when launching National Condom Week.

35 Sir Peter Hall.

36 Desmond Morris.

37 U Soe Nyunt, of the Burmese ruling State Law and Order Restoration Council, after the military government conceded that the opposition had apparently won the first free elections in 30 years.

38 The Right Revd John Taylor, Bishop of St Albans, on learning that William Hill, the bookmakers, had reduced his odds in the forthcoming choice of a new Archbishop of Canterbury.

39 John Sununu, US President Bush's White House chief of staff, who was invited to teach the Kremlin how to run a democratic presidency.

40 Neil Kinnock, interviewed on BBC 1's *Panorama* programme, concerning the Labour Party's taxation policy.

41 Roy Greenslade, editor of the *Daily Mirror*, on reading the recommendations of the Calcutt committee on newspaper ethics. He said he would take 'a long hard look' at the recommendations; Robert Maxwell, publisher of Mirror Group Newspapers, said that his group's response would be 'measured, not manic'.

42 Frank Braynard, curator of the US Merchant Marine Museum. The Institution, located outside New York, holds the Blue Riband Cup. He was disputing the eligibility of the hovercraft *Hoverspeed Great Britain*.

43 Sir Robin Day, the television interviewer, when shown a 10-point guide, published by the BBC, on how broadcast interviews should be conducted.

44 King Fahd of Saudi Arabia, referring to the death of 1426 Muslim pilgrims in a stampede in a tunnel near the holy Muslim city of Mecca during this year's Haj (pilgrimage).

45 Dr David Owen, leader of the now defunct SDP, on his political career.

46 Keith Richards, lead guitarist of the Rolling Stones group, who had cut a finger, preventing his playing at a Wembley Stadium concert and forcing the cancellation of the concert.

47 The Prince of Wales, addressing by video a conference held by the Royal College of General Practitioners in London, during which, while praising orthodox medical practices, he urged greater tolerance of, and co-operation with, qualified complementary practices, such as chiropratic and homeopathic treatment.

48 Dr George Carey, Archbishop of Canterbury designate and supporter of Arsenal football club, of himself.

49 Dick Douglas, director of Bibles and liturgical publishing at Hodder & Stoughton, the publishing company shortly to bring out a high-technology Bible.

50 President George Bush of the USA, whose convoluted sentences and fractured syntax gave rise to the derogatory term 'Bushspeak'.

51 Virginia Bottomley, the health minister, when calling for facilities to be made available for mothers to breastfeed in public places.

52 Ijaz ul-Haq, son of General Zia, the late military ruler of Pakistan, who returned home after the dismissal of the Bhutto administration, to 'carry on my father's legacy'.

53 President Saddam Hussein of Iraq.

54 Lord Denning, aged 91, former Master of the Rolls, as quoted in *The Spectator* following an interview conducted by A. N.Wilson.

55 Sir Claus Moser, president of the British Association for the Advancement of Science, during a speech to the association in which he claimed that British standards in education no longer matched those of continental Europe, Japan, or, in higher education, the United States.

56 Lord Denning, former Master of the Rolls, on his intention to support 180 villagers of Lasham in their fight to prevent the council's turning a picturesque footpath into a road.

57 President George Bush, speaking in Rhode Island about the Middle East Gulf crisis.

58 Ernest Saunders, during the 'Guinness Case' trial, to a suggestion of his involvement in a £5.8 million share deal.

59 Mr Justice Henry, when sentencing three of the four defendants in the 'Guinness Case' at Southwark Crown Court.

60 Brian Keenan, after he had been released from four and a half years' imprisonment as a hostage in Beirut

1 (8/3/90) Why should a photograph of a man slicing salami feature prominently in *The Times*?

4 (20/4/90) Who is this genial man of the cloth and why does he associate with so many dogs?

2 (24/3/90) What nationality are these men and for what are they employed?

5 (15/6/90) Who is this man and why is he posing in military attire?

3 (3/4/90) What have these three men in common, apart from their sartorial tastes?

6 (25/6/90) What have these men in common, and where are they?

1 Mr Mohamed Fayed is seen in the Harrods food hall. It had just been announced that the Fayed brothers were to be allowed to keep Harrods, despite a damning official report which said they had lied persistently to win approval for their £615 million takeover of the House of Fraser stores group.

2 They are senior members of Taiwan's National Assembly, seen snoozing during a session in Chungshan Hall, a day after thousands of students ended a protest calling for reform of the country's geriatric political leadership.

3 They were among the 339 people arrested after violence erupted during a Community Charge demonstration in central London.

4 The Rev Eric Evans, the Dean of St Paul's Cathedral, joined his canine friends for a 10-minute sit-in in aid of ITV's charity telethon.

5 Professor David Chandler, head of War Studies and International Affairs at the Royal Military Academy Sandhurst, will take the part of a French general in a re-enactment of the Battle of Waterloo at the site of Wellington's victory to mark the 175th anniversary of the decisive engagement.

6 All are field marshals: (left to right) Lord Bramall, Sir Roland Gibbs, Lord Carver and Sir John Stanier. They were at the Royal Military Academy Sandhurst for the unveiling of a stained glass window memorial to Field Marshal Lord Harding of Petherton.

1 (30/12/89) In what way did *The Times* theatrical notices alter dramatically in 1990?

2 (30/12/89) What part did Wally K. Daly play on the air in the Radio Four adaptation of *Treasure Island*?

3 (30/12/89) About the creation of which classic television series did the film *Fellow Traveller* concern itself?

4 (30/12/89) A dramatization of which famous Old Bailey trial was broadcast on Radio 4 on Monday 1 January?

5 (9/1/90) Which was the most popular Christmas (1989) television programme, attracting 21.77 million viewers?

6 (9/1/90) Who returned to the London stage, in a premiere of what, by whom, at the Almeida Theatre today?

7 (9/1/90) An English actor and comedian died on 8 January after a long battle against Parkinson's Disease. He had latterly lived in reduced circumstances, but in April 1989 a theatrical gala concert was staged at the Theatre Royal, Drury Lane, to provide for his necessities. Who was he? How much was raised?

8 (20/1/90) Which cartoon cat celebrated his 71st birthday by appearing in a feature-length film?

9 (20/1/90) Which autobiographical fantasy film, first released in 1963, was re-released this month?

10 (3/2/90) Name the three featured stars of Sidney Lumet's new film *Family Business*.

11 (3/2/90) What proposed financial measure caused dismay to the theatrical profession in February?

12 (6/2/90) What controversial RSC production, adapted from a futuristic novel, opened at the Barbican to a generally lukewarm response? And who wrote the music?

13 (13/2/90) Which London theatre was destroyed by fire, caused probably by an electrical fault?

14 (13/2/90) Which character was written out of the radio programme, *The Archers*?

15 (15/2/90) Who was named as successor to Terry Hands as artistic director of the Royal Shakespeare Company?

16 (23/2/90) BBC2 showed Billy Wilder's *Double Indemnity* as a tribute to its recently deceased female star. Who was she?

17 (24/2, 3/3/90) Where did Alan Whicker alight for his latest series of *Whicker's World*?

18 (24/2/90) A revival of which Scandinavian stage classic opened at the National on 28 February?

19 (2/3/90) What British television programme, introduced as a novelty in Middle America in the autumn of 1989, became a regular feature, attracting rave reviews?

20 (13/3/90) ITV began a prestigious three-part documentary on an outstanding figure of the twentieth century. Who was he?

21 (17/3/90) Tickets for whose three concerts at the London Arena in March were claimed to have sold out in eight minutes?

22 (17/3/90) What was this year's Royal Film Performance, who directed it, and of what is it a remake?

23 (17/3/90) What award was given to Mr Andreas Whittam Smith by *What the Papers Say*, television's longest-running current affairs programme?

24 (24/3/90) What proportion of the British public, according to Gallup interviews for Channel 4 *Right to Reply* programme, felt that full frontal nudity and explicit sex scenes in films were acceptable on television, at least late at night?

25 (28/3/90) At the 'Oscar' awards ceremony, who were voted actor and actress of the year and in which films? Which picture won the 'Film of the Year' trophy?

1 After 34 years with *The Times*, Irving Wardle relinquished his post as chief theatre critic. His final article appeared on 30 December, 1989.

2 The parrot.

3 *The Adventures of Robin Hood*.

4 The Old Bailey trial of 1960 when Penguin Books was charged under the Obscene Publications Act for publishing D. H. Lawrence's *Lady Chatterley's Lover*.

5 The film *Crocodile Dundee* on BBC.

6 Glenda Jackson in *Scenes from an Execution* by Howard Barker.

7 Terry Thomas. £75,000.

8 Felix the Cat, created by Pat O'Sullivan and Otto Messner, who first appeared in *Feline Follies* in 1919.

9 Frederico Fellini's *8½*.

10 Sean Connery, Dustin Hoffman and Matthew Broderick.

11 Actors would be removed from self-employed status and taxed under Schedule E (PAYE).

12 *A Clockwork Orange*, adapted from the novel by Anthony Burgess. Ludwig van Beethoven and Bono and The Edge from the band U2.

13 The Savoy Theatre.

14 Nigel Pargetter.

15 Adrian Noble.

16 Barbara Stanwyck.

17 Hong Kong.

18 *Peer Gynt* by Ibsen.

19 Prime Minister's question time in the House of Commons.

20 Josef Stalin.

21 David Bowie.

22 *Always*, directed by Steven Speilberg. The film is a remake of Victor Fleming's *A Guy Named Joe* (1943).

23 Andreas Whittam Smith, editor of *The Independent*, was named 'Editor of the Year'.

24 Two-thirds of those interviewed.

25 The Academy of Motion Picture Arts and Sciences Awards were won by Daniel Day-Lewis for his performance in *My Left Foot*, and Jessica Tandy in *Driving Miss Daisy*. The latter film was chosen as 'Film of the Year'.

26 (4/4/90) Who asked *European Culture: Does It Exist?* on BBC Radio 3?

27 (5/4/90) Which group of popular entertainers go by the names Leonardo, Michelangelo, Raphael and Donatello?

28 (7/4/90) Of which controversial Radio 1 broadcaster was the following said: '[his] humour is constantly short-circuiting itself and treating ideas like clockwork toys to be wound up for the pleasure of seeing where they will fall'?

29 (7/4/90) The revival of which latterday western opened at the Camden Plaza? Who directed it, and what was the title of his new film, premiered in London two months later, and shown on television in August?

30 (9/4/90) Which musical won the Laurence Olivier Award for its class, despite strong opposition?

31 (13/4/90) Who wrote the play *The Piano Lesson* and what prize did it win?

32 (23/4/90) The return of *Song and Dance* to the West End meant that composer Andrew Lloyd Webber had five shows running simultaneously in the capital. Who are the two stars of the show?

33 (24/4/90) To whom did Greta Garbo leave her entire estate, thought to be worth tens of millions of dollars?

34 (27/4/90) Harold Fielding Ltd went into voluntary liquidation after the failure of which theatrical production?

35 (2/5/90) Which West End production was cancelled to allow an investigation into the safety of the artists during performance?

36 (3/5/90) On what grounds did a prosecutor in Alabama, USA, seek to extradite the directors of a New York broadcasting company to face criminal charges?

37 (4/5/90) Which member of the British royal family became the first to appear in a television advertisement and for what purpose?

38 (4/5/90) Why was journalist Mr Duncan Campbell awarded £50,000 libel damages and £50,000 legal costs against the BBC, together with a full apology to him at peak viewing time, the first occasion, it is believed, that the BBC has paid damages over a work of fiction which clearly identified and vilified a recognizable person?

39 (12/5/90) Which film was chosen for the gala opening of this year's Cannes Film Festival?

40 (12/5/90) About the making of which film is Clint Eastwood's latest release, *White Hunter, Black Heart*?

41 (18/5/90) What centuries-old tradition was broken in this year's production of the Passion Play at Oberammergau, West Germany, where it has been staged every decade for 360 years?

42 (19/5/90) A new production, directed by Sir Peter Hall, of an outstanding European play opened at The Phoenix. What was it?

43 (19/5/90) The National Theatre launched a production of what to mark whose 75th birthday?

44 (19/5/90) Name the original author, the executive producer, the director and the star of the film *The Witches*.

45 (21/5/90) BBC launched a week of programming around environmental issues. What was the general title of the event?

46 (16/6/90) What was the outcome of a Downing Street seminar, chaired by the Prime Minister and attended by 20 leading figures in the film industry?

47 (18/6/90) Who won the BBC television programme *Mastermind* 1990?

48 (20/6/90) Prince Edward announced that he was leaving Andrew Lloyd Webber's production company, the Really Useful Group, to do what?

49 (23/6/90) Three new productions of *King Lear* were compared. Identify the lead actors, and the companies involved.

50 (23/6/90) *My Indecision Is Final* was the title of a candid memoir. Whose, about what?

26 Anthony Burgess.

27 The Teenage Mutant Ninja Turtles, a mania stemmed from Ninja turtles, originally featured in a comic strip, loud-mouthed, pizza-eating turtles who supposedly live in New York sewers. A television show featuring these human-sized turtles appears daily on 130 television stations; turtle figures were the third biggest selling toy in the United States last Christmas. A film has also been made of them, consisting mainly of their non-stop violence.

28 Victor Lewis-Smith.

29 *McCabe and Mrs Miller* (1972), by Robert Altman. *Vincent and Theo*, a treatment of the life of Vincent Van Gogh.

30 *Return to the Forbidden Planet*, which beat the favourite *Miss Saigon*. Sub-titled 'Shakespeare's Rock Opera', a musical Space Age version of *The Tempest*, it had opened at the Belgrade Theatre, Coventry, and had not at first been expected to be transferred to the West End.

31 The black American playwright, August Wilson. The play won a Pulitzer Prize for drama, the second that Wilson had been awarded. His earlier Pulitzer Prize was for his play *Fences* in 1987.

32 Wayne Sleep and Marti Webb.

33 Her niece, a Mrs Grae Feisfield, the daughter of her late brother.

34 *Someone Like You*, conceived and co-written by Petula Clark, who also starred in the show, which closed after only five weeks. It is thought that the company had earlier lost more than £3 million on the musical *Ziegfeld*. Mr Fielding, who first became a West End producer 48 years before, was undismayed and determined to start again.

35 The National Theatre's production of Stephen Sondheim's musical *Sunday in the Park with George*. The previous evening performance had been called off when a wooden tree, which needed to be 'flown' off stage on pulleys, fell from its hook, narrowly missing an actor.

36 For transmitting sexually explicit films from space into his county. The prosecution, the first to pit present-day technology against 19th-century obscenity laws, poses ominous strictures for telecommunications conglomerates.

37 The Duke of Edinburgh, who will explain to the TV character Alf Garnett, played by Warren Mitchell, why he should support the British Sports Trust, an organisation which helps young people to enter sport.

38 BBC 2 admitted in the High Court that it had branded him as unreliable and as an transvestite shop lifter in a fictional play, *Here is the News*.

39 *Dreams* by Akira Kurosawa.

40 John Huston's *The African Queen*.

41 For the first time, a married woman with two children was cast as the Virgin Mary. Hitherto, married women and those aged more than 35 years were excluded from rôles in the play.

42 Ibsen's *The Wild Duck*.

43 *The Crucible*. Arthur Miller.

44 Roald Dahl, Jim Henson, Nicholas Roeg and Angelica Huston.

45 *One World Week*.

46 A £5 million cash injection for British film makers and the establishment of a working party to examine the problems facing the industry. Film production had fallen last year to its lowest point for half a century.

47 David Edwards of Uttoxeter, who is a science master and an amateur sword dancer.

48 To establish a theatre production company, with five of his colleagues.

49 Brian Cox at the National Theatre, John Wood with the RSC at Stratford, Richard Briers with the Renaissance Theatre Company.

50 Jake Eberts, formerly chief executive of Goldcrest Films, recounting the success and sudden failure of the company.

51 (29/5/90) How much money for charities was raised by Independent Television's bonanza, *Telethon '90*, after 27 hours of continuous transmission?

52 (7/7/90) A cult musical of the 1970s re-opens at the Piccadilly Theatre this month. What is it, and who wrote it?

53 (7/7/90) *Darlings of the Gods*, a mini-series made by Thames Television, focussed on the relationship between which three thespians?

54 (7/7/90) 24 boys star in a new remake of whose film, based on whose original novel?

55 (7/7/90) Two films sharing the same title have been premiered this year. Both are set in Japan. What was the common title, and, in brief, what were they about?

56 (14/7/90) *Tie Me Up, Tie Me Down* is 'the latest mischief from the *enfant terrible* of the Spanish cinema'. Who is he?

57 (14/7/90) Who appeared as Isherwood's *The Single Man* at the Greenwich Theatre?

58 (1/8/90) Which film opened at two West End cinemas on Friday 27 July and over the week-end made £175,000—the biggest two-screen box office opening Great Britain has seen—and was the most expensive epic yet produced, costing $70 million (£39 million)?

59 (4/8/90) Who resigned as artistic director of Glyndebourne Festival Opera and why?

60 (13/8/90) The Times *Diary* reported that publicists were promoting the science fiction thriller film *Total Recall* by running an interactive phone-in competition, the prize being a trip to Mars. To where in fact would successful contestants win an expenses paid trip?

61 (13/8/90) Which film, made in 1966 and scheduled for reshowing by BBC 1 on Sunday 12 August, was replaced with another at almost the last moment and why?

62 (15/8/90) Which play, written by whom, whose West End run was cancelled in 1968 after a libel suit, is to be revived and how is this now legally possible?

63 (16/8/90) Why did the film star Charlton Heston resign from American Equity, the actors' union?

64 (20/8/90) How did the nicknamed 'Bashir of Baghdad' come to prominence?

65 (25/8/90) 'This is Shakespeare in jackboots.' What is?

66 (25/8/90) A new film by the American cult film-maker David Lynch opened in London this week. Name the film; also, name his television series which is being shown currently in the US, and, it is hoped, will be broadcast in Britain later this year.

67 (25/8/90) Derek Jacobi stars in a revival of a French play on a British subject at the Old Vic. Name the play and its author.

68 (27/8/90) In what way did 5 take over 2 in an attempt to please the under 30s?

69 (1/9/90) *Memphis Belle*, a new film produced by David Puttnam, opens shortly. It is inspired by a wartime documentary, directed by whom?

70 (1/9/90) Joan Collins returns to the London stage in a revival of what?

71 (15/9/90) In what country is *Greek Tragedy*, a new play at the Theatre Royal, Stratford East, set? Who directed it?

72 (15/9/90) Which members of which notable theatrical family are centrally involved in a revival of J. B. Priestley's *Time and the Conways*, at the Theatr Clwyd, Mold, in North Wales?

73 (18/9/90) Who has designed the costumes for a revival of Jean Anouilh *The Rehearsal* at the Almeida?

74 (19/9/90) The adventures of which comic book hero began a five part adaptation on Radio 4 today?

75 (19/9/90) *Portrait of a Marriage* is a four-part television dramatisation of whose unusual relationship?

51 A record £24,127,917, topping the £23 million raised by the same means in 1988. The money will be disbursed to charities around the country, chosen by ITV regions.

52 *The Rocky Horror Show*, by Richard O'Brien.

53 Laurence Oliver, his wife Vivien Leigh, and the young actor they met on a 1948 Old Vic tour of Australia, Peter Finch.

54 *The Lord of the Flies*, by William Golding, first filmed by Peter Brook in 1963.

55 *Black Rain*. The first, an American-made thriller, placed an American detective in a violent mystery in modern Japan. The second, directed by Shohei Imamura, examined the human consequences of the Hiroshima atom bomb.

56 Pedro Almodovar.

57 Alec McCowen.

58 *Total Recall*, starring the bodybuilder/actor Arnold Schwarzenegger, who is thought to have received $10 million and an undisclosed percentage for his contribution.

59 Sir Peter Hall, who will give up the post at the end of the present season rather than at the end of next year's season, as previously scheduled. His early departure is believed to have been in part induced by his strained relationship with the Glyndebourne administration over a non-traditional production of *The Magic Flute* earlier this year by the American stage director, Peter Sellars.

60 Scrutiny of the small print reveals it to be Mars, Pennsylvania.

61 *Khartoum*, a concoction of historical fact and Hollywood licence, told of the confrontation in 1884–5 between General Gordon (Charlton Heston) and the Mahdi (Laurence Olivier), who besieged the British general in the Sudan. Only a minute before the scheduled screening at 3pm, a BBC special news item reported that the Foreign Office feared that a Briton, trying to escape from Kuwait, which had recently been occupied by Iraq, had been shot by Iraqi soldiers. 'With the safety of British people in the Gulf possibly at risk we felt it would have been insensitive to go ahead with the film,' a BBC spokesman explained.

62 *Soldiers*, by the German dramatist Rolf Hochhuth, in which it was suggested that Sir Winston Churchill was involved in a plot to assassinate General Sikorski, head of the Polish government in exile during the Second World War. Sikorski was killed in an air crash off Gibraltar while being flown in an RAF aircraft by a Czech pilot, Captain Edward Prchal, who survived the incident. Mr Prchal sued the playwright, the producers, and Andre Deutsch, publisher of a book based on the theory. He died in 1984, leaving the way open for the play's production.

63 In protest over the union's decision to ban Jonathan Pryce, a Welsh actor, from performing in the proposed Broadway production of *Miss Saigon* because he is not Eurasian. The musical's production is presently in jeopardy over this casting issue, but the following day Equity reversed its decision, conceding that it 'had applied an honest and moral principle in an inappropriate manner.'

64 Like 'Lord Haw-Haw' of Second World War infamy, his honeyed tones are beamed to Saudi Arabia with the object of undermining the morale of troops based there during the Gulf crisis. The announcer uses, however, fractured English and incomprehensible phrases, such as 'Why do you come to a land which you are not ameliorated to its people and its nature . . .'

65 Richard Eyre's new production of *Richard III*, starring Ian McKellan, at the Lyttleton, National Theatre.

66 *Wild at Heart* and *Twin Peaks*.

67 *Kean* by Jean-Paul Sartre.

68 BBC new Radio 5 was launched, the first new national radio network for 23 years. The station is aimed primarily at young listeners and sports fans, and has taken over Radio 2's former medium wave network.

69 William Wyler.

70 Noel Coward's *Private Lives*, in which she takes on the Gertrude Lawrence role of Amanda.

71 Australia; it concerns Greek immigrants in the suburbs of Sydney. The play is the latest creation of improvisational writer/director Mike Leigh.

72 The Oliviers; Lord Olivier's widow, Joan Plowright, and daughters Tamsin and Julie Kate appear in the production, which is directed by his son, Richard. Tamsin's boyfriend Simon Dutton also appears in the play.

73 Fashion designer Jasper Conran.

74 Superman.

75 Harold Nicolson, his wife Vita Sackville-West, and her lover Violet Trefusis.

1 This year, which two professional writers were to feature prominently in elections to determine national leadership?

2 (5/1/90) Which novelist wrote the greatest number of books most in demand from public libraries in 1989,

3 (6/1/90) Which emigré Russian author planned to publish in the Soviet Union a glossary of ancient Russian words and rare dialect?

4 (8/1/90) A cache of some 1500 manuscripts, including letters from Jane Austen, Charlotte Bronte. Catherine the Great and Berlioz, was found stored in a cupboard in what building?

5 (20/1/90) Which holy medieval manuscript was reproduced in a limited facsimile edition and offered for sale at £8,950 each copy?

6 (25/1/90) Who won the 1989 Whitbread Book of the Year prize and for what book?

7 (31/1/90) On 31 January, *The Times* republished a spoof crossword that had first appeared in 1940. Who had composed it?

8 (3/2/90) Which elusive US novelist published his first novel for 17 years?

9 (3/2/90) A review appeared in *The Times* of new editions of three major American novels: *Last Exit to Brooklyn*, *Deliverance* and *The Lost Weekend*. Who wrote them, and who directed film adaptations of each?

10 (13/2/90) Almost exactly one month after her concert appearances in London, *The Times* reviewed the autobiography of Norma Delois Egstrom. By what stage name is she better known?

11 (13/2/90) It was announced that a certain sector of government funding would be increased. About 15,000 writers would benefit. For what would they receive the money?

12 (14/2/90) Who followed in his father's footsteps by being appointed editor of *The Spectator* magazine?

13 (17/2/90) *Prisoner of Love*, a posthumous autobiographical book, was published this month. Who wrote it?

14 (24/2/90) Subtitles of two books published this month: *Alcohol and the American Writer* by Tom Dardis and *Cyril Connolly and the World of Horizon* by Michael Sheldon. What were the main titles?

15 (28/2/90) Who was paid 'very substantial compensation' and awarded the full legal costs of bringing a libel action concerning a passage in a book, *The Greatest Treason*, about the Burgess and Maclean spy affair?

16 (3/3/90) The very first in a popular series of comic adventure books has finally been published in English. What is it, and when was it first published in its native language?

17 (3/3/90) Owen Chadwick and Michael De-la-Noy both published biographical books on the same subject this month. Who was it?

18 (3/3/90) What was unusual about the subject of Tony Parker's book *Life after Life*?

19 (8/3/90) Of whom was Maureen Borland's book, *Wilde's Devoted Friend*, the first full-length biography?

20 (10/3/90) The Russian politician, Boris Yeltsin, chose what title for his autobiography?

21 (10/3/90) Name the English bookshop at 12 Rue de l'Odéon which formed the focal point for many American and English writers and artists in Paris in the 1920s. Who was the owner?

22 (29/3/90) Both Czechs and Slovaks agreed to expunge the name Czechoslovak Socialist Republic. How did they differ in choosing a replacement name?

23 (31/3/90) In what way did the discovery of two cannon balls fired at the Hebridean island of Islay by a marauding American privateer during the Anglo-American War of 1812–14 provide the basis for a new ending to Robert Louis Stevenson's unfinished novel, *St Ives*?

24 (31/3/90) What 'club' was started in 1930, including Ngaio Marsh and Agatha Christie among its first alumni, and is this year celebrating its Diamond Jubilee?

25 (31/3/90) Four volumes by the 1988 Nobel Prize-winner for literature were reviewed. Who is he?

26 (29/3/90) In what way did the 9th Regiment Army Air make life easier for Brontë enthusiasts?

27 (5/4/90) The long-awaited 4th volume in the official history of what, edited by F. M. Hinsley and C. A. G. Simkins, was published this week?

28 (7/4/90) What was unusual about the manner in which a new concordance to the works of Robert Burns was assembled?

29 (7/4/90) Volumes 10 and 11 of whose diaries, spanning the years 1881–1886, were published by Oxford University Press at £60 each?

30 (2/5/90) What first edition fetched $561,000 (£350,000) at a sale at Sotheby's New York, breaking a world record in price?

1 Václav Havel, in Czechoslovakia, and Mario Vargas Llosa in Peru.

2 Catherine Cookson, who had 32 titles in the 100 books most borrowed.

3 Aleksandr Solzhenitsyn.

4 The headquarters of the Torquay Natural History Society.

5 *The Book of Kells*, published by Fine Art Facsimile of Switzerland.

6 Richard Holmes, for the first volume of his study of Coleridge, entitled *Coleridge, Early Visions*.

7 Sir Max Beerbohm; only four of the questions had a logical answer.

8 Thomas Pynchon. *Vineland* this year and *Gravity's Rainbow* (1973).

9 *Last Exit to Brooklyn* (1964) was written by Hubert Selby Jr. and filmed by Uli Edel (1989); *Deliverance* (1970) was writted by James Dickey and filmed by John Boorman (1972); *The Lost Weekend* (1944) was written by Charles Jackson and filmed by Billy Wilder (1945).

10 Peggy Lee.

11 The authors would receive payments from government funding of the Public Lending Right.

12 Dominic Lawson, son of Nigel Lawson, who edited the magazine in the 1960s.

13 Jean Genet.

14 *The Thirsty Muse* and *Friends of Promise* respectively.

15 Lady Avon, widow of Lord Avon, the statesman Anthony Eden. The publishers, Century Hutchinson, recalled all copies of the book and pulped all those retrieved.

16 Hergé's *Tintin in the Land of the Soviets*, first published in 1929.

17 Former Archbishop of Canterbury Michael Ramsey.

18 The book comprised interviews with twelve convicted murderers.

19 Robert Ross, the art critic, gallery director and writer.

20 *Against the Grain*. The UK edition was translated by Michael Glenny and published by Jonathan Cape.

21 Shakespeare and Company, owned by Sylvia Beach.

22 The Slovaks, who comprise some one-third of the population, demanded that the country should be named the Federation of Czecho-Slovakia; the Czechs wanted the name Czechoslovak Republic because, they argued, the hyphen would be divisive.

23 The novel had been completed in 1897 by Sir Arthur Quiller-Couch, but he refused to believe that American privateers plied British waters during the conflict. The new end to Stevenson's novel, published in April, was re-written by Mrs Jenni Calder, one of Stevenson's biographers, the discovered cannon balls altering the Quiller-Couch version.

24 The Collins Crime Club.

25 The Egyptian Naguib Mahfouz.

26 They used a Lynx helicopter to airlift a 10-inch thick stone slab into position, restoring the Brontë Bridge across South Dean Beck on the Brontë Way footpath near Haworth, West Yorkshire; the bridge is about a mile from Top Withers house, reputed to be the Wuthering Heights of Emily Brontë's novel.

27 The British intelligence services in the Second World War.

28 *Burns A–Z: The Complete Word-Finder*, which lists some 15,000 key words, 80,000 quotations, and cross-references to all his works, was assembled with the aid of a computer.

29 Gladstone.

30 Shakespeare's *Lucrece*, which fetched the highest price ever for a Shakespeare quarto, twice the expected sum, due doubtless to its being the only obtainable copy of the Bard's earliest obtainable work.

31 (10/5/90) What direct connection is there between the authors Raymond Chandler and Robert B. Parker?

32 (12/5/90) Which English monarch was reported as breeding albino ferrets, which were given away as gifts?

33 (12/5/90) *The Last Modern* by James King is a biography of whom?

34 (12/5/90) *The Good, the Bad and the Ugly* was lambasted in *The Times*. Whose 'personal testament' was the book?

35 (19/5/90) A new book, *The King's Wife* by Robert Gray, examines the lives of five Queen Consorts. Name them.

36 (19/5/90) Charles Hamilton, a prolific popular writer, used a variety of pen-names: Owen Conquest, Martin Richards, Ralph Redway and Hilda Richards. Can you give his most famous pen-name?

37 (22/5/90) Whose London residence between 1748 and 1759, has now been reopened to the public after a six-month refurbishment?

38 (26/5/90) *Off the Road* was reviewed; who wrote it, and who is it about?

39 (26/5/90) Whose 28th novel was favourably reviewed and summed up: 'You can put your shirt on this one—straight'?

40 (26/5/90) A new edition of a novel first published in 1940, by Richard Wright, was favourably compared to Drieser's *An American Dream*, to Ralph Ellison's *Invisible Man* and to James Baldwin's *Another Country*. What is its title?

41 (6/6/90) Which journalist was named Columnist of the Year in the *UK Press Gazette* British press awards?

42 (18/6/90) What did the discovery by the University of Texas of *Finnegans Wake*'s opening chapter in typescript reveal about James Joyce's working methods?

43 (27/6/90) The birthplace home of which English writer, stripped to its foundations a hundred years ago by locals, was excavated so that the site may feature as a tribute to the author?

44 (29/6/90) Which British author was paid a reported £7.2 million by the Dell Publishing Company for two books not yet written or even outlined?

45 (30/6/90) Which British politician entitled his second volume of memoirs *A Sparrow's Flight*?

46 (7/7/90) What United Kingdom tourist attraction was omitted from the latest AA road atlas in roughly 100,000 copies because of a problem at the Spanish printing plant?

47 (7/7/90) Of whom was *Outrageous Fortune* (1900–1940), by Roger Keyes, a biography?

48 (7/7/90) *A Victorian in his world* was the subtitle to a new biography by Richard Mullen. Of whom?

49 (11/7/90) Which British daily newspaper, less than five years after leaving premises in Fleet Street for new ones on the Isle of Dogs, moved its office again and to where?

50 (27/7/90) What is the purpose of the recently published *Royal Mail International Business Travel Guide*?

51 (4/8/90) Which writer, after serving as interim president, was elected the first president of the new Democratic Republic of Hungary?

52 (15/8/90) What advertisement, which greatly increased sales for a Cambridge garden equipment company, published in the *Telegraph Weekend* and *Sunday Express* magazines, prompted 80 complaints and why did it result in a severe rebuke from the Advertising Standards Authority?

53 (17/8/90) In what way did the Soviet Union alter the status of the writer Alexander Solzhenitsyn and 22 other dissidents?

54 (17/8/90) Who was appointed the new editor, in replacement of Peter Cole, of *The Sunday Correspondent*, which is to be relaunched Britain's first 'quality tabloid'?

55 (20/8/90) A survey published yesterday by Mintel, consumer research analysts, shows that British bookbuyers shun fiction, despite 'bestseller' lists, in favour of what literature?

56 (25/8/90) Why were 180,000 volumes of this year's colour edition of Larousse, the world's leading publisher of French dictionaries, recalled?

57 (25/8/90) *The Play of the Eyes* is the newly published third volume of whose autobiography?

58 (25/8/90) Two major new encyclopaedias were launched. Who were the publishers?

59 (1/9/90) The announcement that which favourite children's character was to star in a new £12 million film lead to lengthy debate in *The Times* correspondence columns over his moral character, culminating in a Third Leader?

60 (22/9/90) Name six Booker Prize shortlisted titles and authors. Which have been shortlisted before?

31 Parker has just published his completed version of Chandler's unfinished Marlowe novel *Poodle Springs*.

32 Queen Victoria, according to a feature on *The Complete Book of Ferrets* (Pelham) by Fred Taylor and Val Porter.

33 Herbert Read.

34 Former RIBA president Dr Rod Hackney.

35 Eleanor of Aquitaine, Henrietta Maria, Catherine of Braganza, Caroline of Brunswick and Queen Mary.

36 Frank Richards, author of the *Bunter* books. From a review of *I Say, You Fellows* (Wharton Press by Maurice Hall.)

37 Dr Johnson's in Gough Square, off Fleet Street, where he wrote his great dictionary.

38 Written by Carolyn Cassady, the book is her account of her life with Beat Generation founders Neal Cassady, Jack Kerouac.

39 Dick Francis, of his last novel *Straight*, which has now been published in a large format paperback.

40 *Native Son*.

41 Bernard Levin of *The Times*; he had previously won the award in 1987.

42 The typescript, including handwritten changes, shows that Joyce wrote by adding phrases and words to a final draft rather than by editing them out.

43 Lewis Carroll (Charles Lutwidge Dodgson), who was born in Daresbury, Cheshire, in 1832, the son of the local parson.

44 Ken Follett, the thriller writer.

45 Lord Hailsham; his first volume, published in 1975, was entitled *The Door Wherein I Went*.

46 Loch Lomond; instead of the outline of the loch, the atlas showed several rivers and roads.

47 King Leopold III of the Belgians who, in the author's view, had been traduced for ordering his army to surrender to the Germans in May 1940 and for not taking refuge in the United Kingdom.

48 Anthony Trollope

49 The Daily Telegraph, publisher of *The Daily Telegraph*, the *Sunday Telegraph* and *The Spectator*, will move a quarter of a mile north of its present home to become one of the founder tenants of Canary Wharf, where it will take five floors of the newly completed 800ft skyscraper.

50 The Post Office guide contains pages of detailed information on every country and its customs, stating, among much else, that in Albania a nod of the head means 'no' and a shake 'yes', while in Tonga it is illegal not to wear a shirt in public.

51 Arpad Goncz, aged 63, who served six years of a life term imposed in 1958 by the Communists, was elected by an overwhelming majority in parliament, receiving support from all six parties represented.

52 A partially clothed model, a former Miss Mauritius, dressed as a slave, wearing manacles and chained to a stake in a lawn, appeared beneath the slogan 'Don't be a slave to your garden', which apparently attracted more complaints than any single advertisement for some time.

53 Soviet citizenship, of which they were stripped between 1966 and 1988, was restored by presidential decree, according to a spokesman as 'a way of apologising'.

54 John Bryant, until then deputy editor of *The Times*.

55 Reference books make up one fifth of total book sales (worth £2000 million last year), followed by cookery books at 16 per cent. Other favourite subjects were sport, travel and gardening. Two forms of fiction only—thrillers and romantic novels–were in the top ten categories.

56 A mis-captioned photograph labelled a deadly mushroom 'harmless' and a harmless mushroom 'deadly'.

57 Elias Canetti.

58 Cambridge University Press and Guinness.

59 Beatrix Potter's Peter Rabbit.

60 *An Awfully Big Adventure*, Beryl Bainbridge.
Previously shortlisted for *The Dressmaker* (1973) and *The Bottle Factory Outing* (1974).
Possession, A. S. Byatt.
The Gate of Angels, Penelope Fitzgerald.
Previously shortlisted for *The Bookshop* (1978), and *The Beginning of Spring*, (1988), and winning with *Offshore* 1979).
Amongst Women, John McGahen.
Lies of Silence, Brian Moore.
Previously shortlisted for *The Doctor's Wife* (1976) and *The Colour of Blood* (1987).
Solomon Gursky Was Here, Mordecai Richler.
Previously shortlisted for *St. Urbain's Horseman* (1971).

1 (26/2/90) For what purpose was this building, shortly to be restored, originally constructed?

4 (3/8/90) Where was this photograph taken, and with what project is it connected?

2 (31/5/90) Where are these newly-installed gates and what function do they fulfil?

5 (6/8/90) What is the purpose of these buildings and where are they located?

3 (11/6/90) Where, and what is the function of, this Victorian building, now in decay, and what disputes has it aroused between whom?

1 The last surviving Georgian grandstand in Great Britain, it was built in 1775 by public subscription for £1200 and is sited at Richmond, North Yorkshire. Stones left on the site will be used in the reconstruction.

2 They are the last of 116 lock gates, being lifted into place on the flight of 29 locks at Caen Hill on the Kennet and Avon Canal near Devizes, Wiltshire. Boats will now be able to navigate the 87-mile waterway that first connected the Avon to the Thames in 1810.

3 The Crossness sewage works in London was built 135 years ago. A notable monument to Victorian engineering, it is the subject of a dispute between its owners, Thames Water, and a charity set up to restore it. The charity's chairman said, 'We want to work in the building to make it safe, but Thames say we can't go there because it's not safe'.

4 One of the less-visited sections of Hadrian's Wall; the Government announced the establishment of a task force to reduce tourist pressure on historic monuments and beauty spots, part of which entails making the wall a full-length national trail so that certain areas are no longer overwhelmed by visitors.

5 Fishermen's huts at Hastings, once used for drying nets, were originally built high some 100 years ago to avoid ground rent increases. With the advent of synthetic nets, they have been turned into stores and are now a tourist attraction.

1 (30/12/89) An extraordinary collection created by the former ambassador for the United Arab Emirates went on display at Christie's on 3 January. What did it comprise?

2 (30/12/89) What was unusual about the terms of the Vaughan Bequest of Turner Watercolours to the National Gallery of Scotland?

3 (6/1/90) An exhibition of abstract art by which former member of The Beatles opened at Sotheby's George Street Gallery on 8 January?

4 (20/1/90) Where in London is a suit of elephant armour to be found, for the time being, on display? Who originally acquired it?

5 (22/1/90) A painting by which celebrated artist, on show at a major exhibition at the Royal Academy, was claimed by art expert, Professor Klaus Grimm, to be either a copy or the work of an apprentice?

6 (23/1/90) An appeal was initiated to raise £7.6 million to prevent an important piece of sculpture being exported to the Getty Museum in California. What does it portray? Who was the sculptor?

7 (24/1/90) In January the Tate Gallery's pictures on display were rearranged for the first time since the 1960s. In what way does the new arrangement differ from the old?

8 (24/1/90) Which exhibition of paintings, sculptures, illustrations and videos by artists under 35 opened in Glasgow in January?

9 (3/2/90) Which British painter of portraits and scientific scenes was given a comprehensive exhibition at the Tate Gallery?

10 (3/2/90) What festival of events, celebrating the ancient fire festival Jolablot, was held in York this month.

11 (17/2/90) Which British artist enjoyed a 'selective survey' exhibition at the Tate Gallery, Liverpool from 22 February?

12 (17/2/90) The work of which society, formed in 1855, went on show at The Westminster Gallery from 23 February?

13 (20/2/90) Sixteen huge paintings—average dimensions 12 feet × 6 feet—by Sir David Cameron, Charles Sims, Eric Kennington, John and Paul Nash, Henry Tonks and others were shown together in the first of two exhibitions which ran from February to mid-May. What was their general subject, and where were they displayed? Why were they originally commissioned?

14 (24/2/90) What unusual materials are used by the former Glasgow school artist Mario Rossi?

15 (27/2/90) Which American film actor put on sale at Christie's, New York, 19 important works of contemporary art, part of a collection, including canvasses by Picasso, Braque, Chagall and others?

16 (2/3/90) What unusual art exhibition opened at the British Museum on 9th March?

17 (3/3/90) An exhibition of whose work, subtitled 'Impressionism, Landscape and Rural Labour,' toured Birmingham City Museum and Art Gallery, and the Burrell Collection Glasgow?

18 (10/3/90) Which sculptor, who died on 2 March, was the only artist to complete busts from life of four popes and who were they?

19 (16/3/90) Which British artist painted the watercolour that established the record watercolour price of £473,000 at Sotheby's? What royal building does it portray?

20 (17/3/90) Which British artists were featured in a show of work selected from the Saatchi Collection?

21 (19/3/90) Where did a massive art theft take place in the United States and how was it accomplished?

22 (22/3/90) The restoration of which major masterpiece of world art has now been completed after ten years work?

23 (29/3/90) What were the two main reasons that caused the secretary-general of the Arts Council, Mr Luke Rittner, to resign in March?

24 (31/3/90) What are the 'Sokolov Archives', which were auctioned at Sotheby's in London?

25 (31/3/90) The work of which German artist, noted for painting figures upside-down, went on exhibition at Anthony d'Offay in April?

26 (31/3/90) What was the subject of *The People's Palace* exhibition which opened in London this month?

27 (3/4/90) Why did the Mayor of Jerusalem, take five empty suitcases to Paris?

28 (7/4/90) What painting at the Rijksmuseum was sprayed with sulphuric acid by a vandal?

29 (7/4/90) Jeff Banks has given his services free to rework the uniform of which institution?

30 (7/4/90) Discoveries by which celebrated archaeologist and Asian expert went on display at the British Museum in April?

1 A priceless collection of European gold- and silverware built up by Mohamed Al-Tajir.

2 They may only be exhibited in the month of January.

3 Stuart Sutcliffe, the original bass guitarist, who died of a brain tumour in 1962, aged 21.

4 At the National Museum of Arms and Armour, The Tower of London. It was brought back to England by Clive in the 1750s.

5 Frans Hals. The painting in question was *Portrait of a Woman holding a Fan*, one of the 28 of the 68 works on display that Grimm found suspect. This view was disputed by other authorities.

6 *The Three Graces* by Antonio Canova.

7 Pictures are now displayed chronologically, so that British art is no longer exhibited separately from the rest.

8 The British Art Show, the third of these five-yearly events.

9 Joseph Wright of Derby.

10 The Jorvik Viking Festival.

11 Francis Bacon.

12 The Society of Women Artists.

13 All were depictions of war on the Western Front (1914–18). They were displayed at the Imperial War Museum, London SEI. They had been commissioned for a chapel of remembrance which was never built and had never before been seen together because of their great size.

14 Iron rust and gold dust.

15 Kirk Douglas. The works reflected the discernment of his wife, who had started the collection before their marriage.

16 Entitled 'Fake? The Art of Deception', it comprised objects that had deceived experts into believing them genuine and original.

17 Camille Pissarro.

18 Arthur Fleischmann; the popes were Pius XII, John XXIII, Paul VI and John Paul II. Fleischmann, born a Hungarian, pioneered the use of perspex in sculpture.

19 Turner. Hampton Court Palace.

20 Lucian Freud, Frank Auerbach and Richard Deacon.

21 Thieves, dressed as policemen, overpowered guards at a Boston museum and escaped with works by Rembrandt, Degas, Manet and others. Experts thought that the total value of the stolen paintings could be as much as £130 million.

22 The Sistine Chapel ceiling, by Michelangelo.

23 He resigned over the Government changes to art funding and the reshaping of the Arts Council that would ensue, and also because he said he did not feel he had the confidence of his chairman, Peter Palumbo. Mr Luke Rittner was 34 at the time of his appointment and to date has been the longest-serving secretary general after seven years in office.

24 Photographic documentation of the last days of the Russian Romanov dynasty, mostly murdered by the Bolsheviks in 1918. The collection, including letters and personal belongings, had been compiled by Nicolai Sokolov for the White Armies.

25 George Baselitz.

26 Fulham Palace, once the home of the Bishop of London.

27 To 'rescue' a painting and over 100 drawings by the Russian Jewish painter, Marc Chagall, from his ailing daughter Ida, for the Israel Museum.

28 Rembrandt's *The Militia Company of Captain Frans Banning Cocq*, commonly called *The Night Watch*. The damage was slight, since only the upper varnish layer was affected.

29 The Girl Guides Association.

30 Sir Marc Stein.

31 (7/4/90) The end of the ILEA meant reorganisation, and new opportunities, for which two educational museums in London?

32 (9/4/90) Why did a grand jury in Cincinnati charge the director of the city's principal art gallery with obscenity and for pornographically depicting minors?

33 (11/4/90) Who was restored to his rightful position in Rome today?

34 (12/4/90) What, encrusted with 20,000 diamonds set in 37lb of gold, is to go on show at the Victoria and Albert Museum this month?

35 (16/4/90) What innovation will be made by the Royal Academy of Arts, starting with their exhibition of Monet's work in September?

36 (25/4/90) Two watercolours by which British artist were found, unframed but in perfect condition, stored in an old chest?

37 (28/4/90) Which major American novelist enjoyed an exhibition of his original and collaborative paintings and graphics at the October Gallery, London, this month? What unusual method did he use for applying paint in certain works?

38 (4/5/90) A record for English silver—£1.15 million at Sotheby's in London—was achieved when what objects were sold by an 'unnamed member of the Royal Family'?

39 (9/5/90) Christie's New York achieved a record sum for a work of pop art when what painting by which artist was sold for how much?

40 (12/5/90) The contents of West Green House, Hartley Wintney, near Basingstoke were auctioned on the premises by Sotheby's. Who was the vendor?

41 (16/5/90) The world record for a work of art rose in New York by nearly $24 million to $82.5 million (£49.7 million) when what painting was sold to a Japanese bidder?

42 (19/5/90) What is Blue John?

43 (16/6/90) Where was a rare and important statue of Queen Senet, of the Twelfth Dynasty, found?

44 (21/6/90) Which world-famous diamond was sold at Christie's in London for £4.07 million, far above the pre-sale estimate of £1.5 million?

45 (21/6/90) Marc Bohan, who after 28 years as designer for Christian Dior in Paris was dismissed last year, was appointed artistic director of which celebrated Mayfair fashion salon?

46 (22/6/90) In a sale at Sotheby's, £1.76 million was paid for a book. What was it?

47 (22/6/90) What, belonging to the inter-war socialite Lady Breckrock, was bought for £154,000 at Sotheby's, and by whom?

48 (23/6/90) The poetry of which British painter went on show at the Tate Gallery this week?

49 (28/6/90) Which London art dealers donated £360,000 towards redecorating which national art museum?

50 (29/6/90) In what way is the National Gallery undergoing its most dramatic rearrangement since it moved into its Trafalgar Square premises in 1838?

51 (6/7/90) What item of furniture set a world record for any piece of furniture at Christie's in London, when it sold for £8.58 million to Barbara Seward Johnson?

52 (7/7/90) What is unusual about the paintings brought together for the current Royal Academy exhibition *Monet in the '90s*?

53 (10/7/90) The Arts Council chose whom as its secretary general to replace Luke Rittner, who resigned in March over the art minister's plan to devolve funding to the regions?

54 (20/7/90) The European Community awarded grants worth £276,000 for which three British architectural restoration projects?

55 (25/7/90) According to a report by US medical experts, what disorder induced the artist Vincent Van Gogh to sever part of his ear and later to kill himself?

56 (2/8/90) Which royal residence was opened to the public for the first time from 6 August following full restoration?

57 (14/8/90) Twelve works by which British artist, whose drawings led to his prosecution for obscenity at Lincoln assizes in 1954, were sold for £380 at a sale at Retford, Nottinghamshire?

58 (18/8/90) The National Trust for Scotland officially admitted that the Glenfinnan monument is almost certainly in the wrong place. What does it commemorate and where should it be?

59 (22/8/90) A collage by John Lennon, entitled *Benny And The Jets*, sold at Sotheby's in London for £23,100, more than four times its estimate. Of what did the 8in by 14in plastic-framed collage consist?

60 (24/8/90) To what position was the London-based artist John Keane appointed and by whom?

93

31 The Geffrye Museum, Hackney and the Horniman Museum.

32 The director had sanctioned an exhibition of photographic works, many containing explicit homosexual images, by the late Robert Mapplethorpe.

33 Marcus Aurelius. His bronze equestrian statue had been removed from the Capitoline Hill for restoration nine years ago.

34 The Argyle Library Egg. The formidable design allows the shell to open, revealing a miniature library inside.

35 For the first time, the academy will sell advance tickets sparing visitors, of whom some 500,000 are expected, from having to queue.

36 Thomas Girton (1775–1802); the views are of Jedburgh Abbey in the Borders and Lydford Castle, Tavistock.

37 William Burroughs, who explored the technique of using firearms for both applying the paint and for creating unusual relief effects.

38 Six handsome George II candle brackets (sconces) fetched the price, breaking the previous record of £980,000 for English silver.

39 Roy Lichtenstein's *Kiss II*, an image of a man and woman embracing, taken from a cartoon strip of 1962, sold for $6 million (£3.6 million).

40 Lord McAlpine.

41 Vincent Van Gogh's *Portrait of Dr Gachet*. The artist completed this study of his friend six weeks before committing suicide.

42 A rare crystalline quartz, found only in Derbyshire, and properly called Derbyshire spar. It is often used in decorative inlay, and larger pieces have been turned into ornamental objects. A rare Blue John goblet appeared at auction in Somerset.

43 In the Royal Collection at Sandringham.

44 The Agra diamond, thought to have adorned the turban of the 16th-century Mogul emperor Babur.

45 The Hartnell fashion house which, less than a decade after the death of its founder, Sir Norman Hartnell, in 1979, had been in decline.

46 A folio edition of Audubon's *Birds of America*, which includes 435 outstanding hand-coloured bird etchings.

47 A diamond necklace, acquired for its antiques collection by Cartier, who originally created the piece. It reached double its high estimate.

48 J. M. W. Turner, some of whose copious verse, written to go with his paintings, has been rediscovered; the verse often illuminates obscurities in his classical and allegorical paintings.

49 Agnews; it the largest single gift made by a picture dealer to a national museum for generations.

50 The collection will no longer be displayed by schools or nationalities but henceforth in chronological sequence, in line with modern academic thinking.

51 The Duke of Beaufort's Badminton cabinet.

52 Many of the paintings share the same subject. The exhibition is made up of Monet's series paintings, in which he investigated changing light and colour effects on particular subjects, notably the façade of Rouen cathedral, haystacks, an avenue of poplars at Giverny and his lily pond.

53 Anthony Everitt, aged 50, who had been Rittner's deputy since 1985 and acting secretary general since the beginning of May.

54 The Conway suspension bridge, Gwynedd, college buildings at Ely Cathedral and Georgian houses in Glasgow.

55 Menière's disease, a condition characterized by periodic and painful ringing in the ears.

56 Frogmore House, in Windsor Home Park.

57 Comic postcards by Donald McGill, depicting, among much else, fat ladies, hen-pecked husbands and silly parsons. They will form part of a museum devoted to McGill's work, due to open at Hay-on-Wye, Powys, by Christmas.

58 The monument, a tower, marks the spot where Bonnie Prince Charlie was thought to have unfurled his white banner before hundreds of clansmen in 1745; general agreement today is that the true site was a knoll on the west bank of the Finnan, a quarter of a mile away.

59 Magazine cuttings of three topless girls on motor cycles, with Andy Warhol heads superimposed. The work was signed and dated 1 October 1974.

60 Keane, who has made conflict a specialist interest, was commissioned by the Imperial War Museum as Great Britain's official war artist in the Gulf.

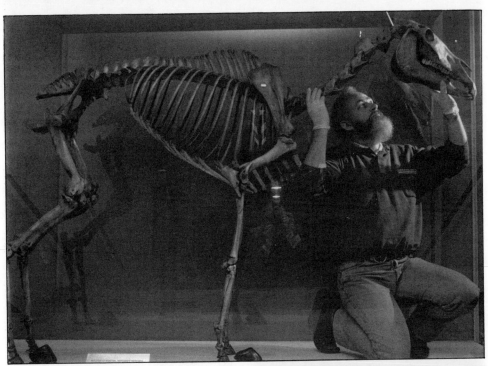

1 (29/3/90) Of which celebrated horse is this the skeleton, being prepared for a war horse exhibition, and where is it normally housed?

2 (30/3/90) What is this machine designed for and what is unusual about it?

3 (7/7/90) What is the name and purpose of this device and where did an example of it go on display?

1 *Märengo*, Napoleon's charger, which is thought to have carried him from the battlefield of Waterloo, is normally on display at the National Army Museum in Chelsea, London.

2 A home-made sewing machine, built by Allied prisoners of war in their efforts to escape from Colditz. The imposing medieval castle is now open to the public.

3 A scold's bridle, designed to 'curb women's tongues that talk too much', is one of the items of torture that went on display at the Tower of London yesterday.